AN INTRODUCTION

TO THE STUDY OF

H Y P N O T I S M

EXPERIMENTAL AND THERAPEUTIC

BY

H. E. WINGFIELD

M.A., M.D., B.C. CANTAB.

CONSULTING PHYSICIAN, ROYAL HANTS COUNTY HOSPITAL;
FORMERLY DEMONSTRATOR OF PHYSIOLOGY IN CAMBRIDGE UNIVERSITY;
EX-PRESIDENT, PSYCHO-MEDICAL SOCIETY;
EX-VICE-PRESIDENT MEDICAL OFFICER OF SCHOOLS ASSOCIATION;
FORMERLY MEDICAL OFFICER TO WINCHESTER COLLEGE;
AUTHOR OF "THE FORMS OF ALCOHOLISM AND THEIR TREATMENT"

ISBN: 979-8-89096-099-3

Printed: June 2023

Published and Distributed By:
Lushena Books
607 Country Club Drive, Unit E
Bensenville, IL 60106
www.lushenabks.com

ISBN: 979-8-89096-099-3

PREFACE TO SECOND EDITION

THIS little book is intended mainly for those who are unacquainted with hypnotism, and aims at providing the reader with sufficient knowledge, both theoretical and practical, to enable him to make use of suggestion in suitable cases.

The fact that the whole of the first edition was sold within a short time of publication encourages me to hope that it fulfilled its aim; and I trust that the present edition, which is published in response to numerous requests, may meet with an equally kind reception.

The phenomena of hypnosis are described in some detail, as I believe that a knowledge of them is essential to the practitioner who uses hypnotism, and though the various theories cannot be criticized in the space at my disposal, I have tried to bring before the reader the chief problems presented by the subject.

To the chapter on treatment I have added an

account of cases bearing on Repressed Memories, and their treatment by hypnotism, a part of the subject which is rapidly increasing in importance in view of Freud's discoveries.

HUGH WINGFIELD.

London,
June, 1920.

CONTENTS

CHAPTER I

INTRODUCTORY

CHAPTER II

THE SUB-CONSCIOUSNESS

CHAPTER III

METHODS OF THE INDUCTION OF HYPNOSIS

CONTENTS

AN INTRODUCTION TO THE STUDY OF HYPNOTISM

CHAPTER I

INTRODUCTORY

First workers in hypnotism—The definition of hypnosis—The phenomena of suggestion—Hypnosis as a state.

FROM immemorial times in the history of mankind the phenomena now classed under the name of hypnotism appear to have been known as isolated facts. Clothed in the guise of the supernatural, regarded sometimes as religious manifestations, sometimes as the results of magic spells or as the work of spirits, they were, of course, unrecognized as a group of effects due to a common and natural cause.

That they had a common origin was first suggested in quite modern times by the experiments of Mesmer at the beginning of the last century. Though he did not comprehend the real character of the phenomena which he produced, yet to him must be ascribed the merit of perceiving that they were due to some natural cause, and of first drawing the attention of men to the problem of their explanation. Mesmer believed

that the phenomena emanated from some kind of
"fluid," and even to this day similar ideas are
common among the general public, and influences
under the names of "will-power" and "animal
magnetism" are invoked to explain the facts.
Mesmer was followed by the surgeons Esdaile,
Elliotson, and Braid, who were attacked by the
majority of the medical profession with that animosity
which invariably greets the discomposing pioneers of
any unfamiliar idea.

To James Braid, the last of the three, belongs the
credit of having first clearly perceived that the
phenomena were due, not to any mysterious or
supernormal emanations, but to the power of suggestion alone, acting on a subject whose suggestibility
has been artificially increased. This view, which has
been abundantly confirmed by Liébeault and the
Nancy school, is now universally accepted. The re-
searches of modern times are mainly attempts to
systematize the phenomena, to explain how it is that
suggestion arrives at such results, and to define the
nature of the condition which is characterized by
such a marked increase of suggestibility. The first
of these aims has to a great extent already been
successfully accomplished, but the others seem a long
way from complete realization.

A suggestion is, of course, simply the implantation
or the development of an idea in the mind of the
person experimented on. The suggestion may come
from without or from the subject himself.

I. The Definition of Hypnosis.

Various attempts have been made to define hypnosis, the condition of artificially increased suggestibility. Some merely express the theories which different authors hold as to the nature of hypnosis. Thus Myers regards suggestion as " a successful appeal to the subliminal self." Sidis defines hypnosis as physiologically "the inhibition of the inhibitory centres," and so on.

Others convey its characteristics as a state in which certain specified phenomena occur ; and this kind of description, in the present state of our knowledge, seems to be open to the least objection.

Bernheim says hypnotism is the production of a psychical condition in which the faculty of receiving impressions by suggestion is greatly increased. But, as Dr. Lloyd Tuckey indicates, this definition does not recognize the extraordinary increase of power to carry out accepted suggestions which is always found in hypnosis.

If I might hazard a definition, I should say that *hypnosis is a psychical condition in which suggestions are not only much more easily accepted, but are also realized with an intensity much greater than is possible to the normal state.* For, however eagerly a man may receive a suggestion in his normal state, it is quite clear that it can be realized only within certain restrictions. Thus, if I suggest to a lady in her normal condition that her dress is on fire, though she may at once accept the suggestion and act accordingly, yet when she sees that her dress is really not burning at all, the suggested idea will be immediately dissipated. But, as we see later, if she be in deep hypnosis, so vivid will be the realization that she will believe she actually sees the flames and smoke, and so becomes subject to a hallucination.

II. The Phenomena of Suggestion.

The following simple experiment will show the effect of a suggestion; I select it because it is the only one I know which practically never fails. Assure anyone that if he takes a pinch of snuff, or even pepper, he will be unable to sneeze, and it will invariably happen that after taking it he cannot do so. Perhaps the suggestion may be made stronger by an offer to bet on the result. It is quite safe to bet; I have never seen the suggestion fail. Yet it is entirely ineffectual to prevent sneezing in a person with a cold.

It is, perhaps, unnecessary to point out that the subject of the experiment will be quite impervious to other suggestions. Thus, if he be told that he must get up from his chair, and cannot help doing so, he will merely smile contemptuously and remain seated where he is. But, as we shall see later on, by what are called hypnotic processes his condition can be so altered that if he be told, for example, that he must get up, or that he cannot get up, he will have to obey the suggestion, even if he resist with all his power.

We shall find, too, that certain groups of suggestions will act readily, while other groups are difficult
to enforce, and that, as the subject is more deeply
hypnotized, these more difficult suggestions are more
and more effective. So it becomes possible to divide
the hypnotic state more or less accurately into stages,
each stage being characterized by the particular group
of phenomena which, can be successfully suggested
therein.

One of the easiest of these suggestions is that the
subject cannot open his eyes. He may struggle with
all his might; in spite of his efforts, he cannot do it.
But here we stumble across a remarkable fact. It not
infrequently happens that the subject is quite convinced that he can open his eyes, and it is only when
he actually attempts it that he realizes by failure
that he cannot do so. Now, it is obvious that the only
effect of the suggestion that he cannot open his eyes
will be the creation of a belief to that effect. But
if the subject have no conscious conviction that he
cannot open his eyes, it is clear that the idea does not
exist in his waking consciousness. Where, then, is the
idea concealed ?

Again, some subjects can be made to pass into
what is known as somnambulism, or the deep state of
hypnosis. When they are awakened from this condition, in the majority of cases we shall find that the
memory of all the events which occurred during this
period has vanished completely. The somnambulist
may have been walking about and talking or acting

under the influence of some suggested delusion or hallucination, but still, on awakening, he will remember absolutely nothing of all this. Yet, if the sleeping condition be again induced, he will remember all the events of his previous sleep. The ideas, then, still continued, but where were they stored? Again, if during his sleep he be commanded to perform some action after he wakes, he will perform it, though he has no conscious recollection of the command. Where, one asks again, was concealed the idea that prompted the action? All through the study of hypnotism this question is the one great problem that constantly confronts us, and the most fascinating part of the whole inquiry is, I think, the hunt for the hiding-place of these apparently lost but really persistent ideas.

III. Hypnosis as a State.

It is often said, after Bernheim's dictum, that hypnosis is nothing but suggestion. But, as Sidis points out in his admirable work on the Psychology of Suggestion, "If hypnosis be nothing but suggestion, by what is it induced? Why, by suggestion. Suggestion is thus its own cause." It seems as though attention had been so concentrated on the striking *phenomena* produced by suggestion that the *condition* of increased suggestibility—or hypnosis, for the terms are synonymous—without which suggestions are absolutely ineffectual, has been ignored. But this increase of suggestibility is merely one of the characteristics of a new psychical condition, which must be accounted for just as much as the effects of the suggestions which this, and this alone, renders possible. The condition appears to be due to some recondite change in the relations of the different parts of consciousness. But this will be better understood when we come to consider the rôle of the sub-consciousness in a later chapter.

Sidis gives the following conditions as essential to the production of hypnosis: fixation of attention, monotony, limitation of voluntary movements, limitation of the field of consciousness, inhibition of all ideas except those upon which attention is to be concentrated. So that hypnosis does, as a matter of fact, depend upon other factors besides mere suggestion. The factors are so simple and natural that it is no wonder that their presence is often unnoticed and their necessity unrecognized, for in making formal suggestions almost anyone would quite instinctively see that they were respected, without being in the least aware of the fact that he was arranging conditions without which his suggestions would be nullified.

Once hypnosis has been induced sufficiently to enable even the simplest suggestions to be effective, there is no doubt the phenomena evoked by the suggestions do of themselves tend to increase suggestibility still further—in other words, to deepen hypnosis. Thus, I hypnotize a subject and ask him to lay his hand on mine, and suggest that he cannot take it off. The suggestion may, of course, succeed or fail. If it fails, I try a suggestion which, I know from experience, can be more easily enforced. I make him shut his eyes, and suggest that he cannot open them. The suggestion probably succeeds. I now tell him that he can open his eyes, and again repeat my first experiment, trying to fix his hand to mine by suggesting that he cannot take it away. This time I succeed. Now, it is quite clear that he is more suggestible than he was when I made the first experiment, and it is equally clear that, had I failed to seal his eyes, I should have found him as refractory as ever to suggestion number one. What, then, has made him more suggestible? Clearly not the suggestion that he could not open his eyes in itself, for if it had failed it would have been powerless to change his condition. It was the *success* of the suggestion that increased his suggestibility : it was the phenomenon of inability to open the eyes that made him more suggestible. To put the matter in another way, successful suggestion will induce hypnotic phenomena, and the phenomena in their turn induce an increased suggestibility.

Many consider that the phenomena of loss of memory and its recovery in subsequent hypnosis is not due to suggestion, but is part and parcel of the deep hypnotic state.

This phenomenon occurs almost constantly in good subjects, without any direct suggestion of amnesia. Bramwell, indeed, states that " with nearly everyone' the idea of hypnosis represents a kind of sleep, with subsequent loss of memory," so that the very suggestion of sleep may be in these cases followed by amnesia. But this does not account for the return of memory during a fresh hypnosis; and, while perhaps it might explain why the suggestion of sleep should produce amnesia in those who expected such a result, this explanation seems hardly applicable to those cases in which somnambulism appears without any suggestion of sleep whatever. It is well known that the production of hallucinations often induces somnambulism, with subsequent amnesia. With many—in fact, with most—of the Cambridge subjects whom I sent into somnambulism I induced it in the first instance by this method, making no suggestion of sleep. I suggested as strongly as I could a visual hallucination, generally of a bright star, and then changed it for another, and so on through a succession of different hallucinations. In almost every case the subject experienced complete amnesia on awaking, followed by a recovery of memory when again hypnotized. It is difficult to see how suggestion could well enter here, and one has to account for the fact that the loss of memory seems to follow the production of hallucinations with a constancy which certainly seems to indicate some causal relation between the two.

It is merely an assumption that because most of the phenomena of hypnotism are due to suggestion, the amnesia and its recovery are necessarily also due to it. But we have no right to make any assumption of this kind; we must abide by the results of experiment.

According to the Nancy experimenters, anæsthesia also may occur spontaneously without suggestion in the deep state. This phenomenon, if correctly stated, would be another case in point.

Post-hypnotic amnesia and the recovery of the memory during subsequent hypnosis (if, as I am inclined to think, not due to suggestion) would seem to reveal a change of *state*, which is rather the consequence of the phenomena of hallucination or of the condition induced by the suggestion of sleep. It seems that, whilst amnesia can be induced by direct suggestion, it may also occur not as a response to that, but in response to, or as a concomitant with, phenomena occasioned by suggestion.

But, in any case, the saying that hypnotism is nothing but suggestion merely begs the whole question. It tells us nothing of the mechanism or of the changes in consciousness which cause the increased suggestibility, and gives no clue to the astounding intensity with which suggestions are realized. In dismissing the subject for the present, it may be worth while to say that even if it were true that all hypnotism is suggestion, that is not a justification for saying that all suggestion is hypnotism, an inference that seems to be sometimes drawn.

It is undeniable that there is still something intellectually unsatisfying in all accounts of the causes of hypnotism, and that further exploration

may end in exciting discoveries. It does seem as if
the process were partially involved in the obscure
problem of personality, and as if some factor at least
were, like other kinds of personal influences and
impressions, the natural and logical product of the
combination of certain psychical qualities which cannot be determined and discriminated as yet, while the
science of psychology. still stammers in its infancy.

CHAPTER II

THE SUB-CONSCIOUSNESS

The sub-consciousness—Evidence of its existence (Sub-conscious chain of memory—Influence of sub-consciousness on waking activities—Motor and sensory automatisms—Passive attention — Multiple personalities) — Relation of primary and secondary consciousness (Its nature—Its bearing on hypnosis).

THOUGH many attempts have been made to explain the phenomena of hypnotism, as yet none of these theories seems completely to cover the facts. On the physiological side numbers of hypotheses have been advanced, but nearly all have been found untenable. The theory of dissociation, which supposes the formation and breaking of links between the various brain centres by a physiological process, has much to be said in its favour : it has been ably discussed in a paper by Dr. McDougall in *Brain*.*

But though there must, of course, be a physiological side to hypnotism, it is in the psychological domain that speculation has been most fruitful. The great result of all investigations has been to emphasize the immense importance of the rôle played by the sub-consciousness, variously termed the "subliminal" or

* "The State of the Brain during Hypnosis." In *Brain*, July, 1908.

12

" secondary " self, consciousness, or personality. The terms secondary or subliminal "self," or "personality," are, I think, objectionable, as they appear to imply the normal existence of something which may properly be conceived as a real separate personality —an assumption for which at present there is not sufficient warrant. It is to Myers that we owe the recognition of the supreme importance of the sub-consciousness, and of the part it takes in producing the phenomena of hypnotism.*

What, then, is the evidence for the existence of this secondary consciousness, and what are its functions and powers?

I. Evidence of Existence of Sub-consciousness.

(a) *Sub-conscious Chain of Memory.*—If a good hypnotic subject, capable of passing into the somnambulistic state, is put to sleep, he may be made to

* In his work on Psychotherapy, the late Professor Munsterberg boldly states that "the sub-conscious" has no existence. This hypothesis compels him to assume that the most complex phenomena generally ascribed to sub-conscious action, such as automatic writing, even when it plainly confesses an intellectual origin, are in reality simply automatic physiological processes, into which no consciousness of any kind enters. It is of the same nature, he says, as the playing of the piano without thought of the special movements of the hands—an automatic reflex. This is strangely like a return to Carpenter's old idea of " unconscious cerebration." It is unlikely that such a view will pass unchallenged. It leaves no satisfactory theory of hypnotism, which Munsterberg attempts to explain as due to abnormal attention to the operator on the part of the subject.

talk, walk about, and see any suggested hallucinatory object. Except for the fact that he exhibits as a rule little or no spontaneity, he might be mistaken for a man in his normal condition, speaking and acting as though he were awake. Yet when he is aroused we find that he has no recollection whatever of what he was doing during his sleep.* If, however, he be sent to sleep again, the memory of the events of his previous hypnosis will have returned, and will persist as long as he remains in that condition, only to vanish again the moment he is re-awakened. More than this, we shall find that during his sleep he remembers the events of his waking life just as well as he does when awake.

We see here one important point of evidence : he has two apparently separate chains of memory—the chain of the sleeping state, which comprises the actions and events of the sleeping and normal life as well ; and, secondly, the chain of the waking state, that which is familiar to us all, and which comprises the events of the waking life alone.

(b) *Influence of Sub-consciousness on Waking Activities.*—But we may now make a fresh experiment. For example, I told a lady who was in somnambulism that after awaking she would turn on the electric lights in my room. I then awakened her, and found that she had no recollection of anything that had passed during her sleep. After about a

* This amnesia can be prevented by suggestion during somnambulism, and the recollection can often be revived by suggestion during the waking state.

minute she began to look at the electric-light switch, and at last said: "Dr. Wingfield, what is that on the wall?" I told her that it was merely the electric-light switch, whereupon she said: "Oh, is it? It is quite different from those in our house. May I try it?" I told her she might, and she turned it on.

Or take another case illustrating the same point, but in a more striking manner. While I was at Cambridge I hypnotized, for experimental purposes, an undergraduate whom we will call X. X, I am sorry to say, was not a hard-working person. It was past the middle of the summer term, and, though he had to sit for the theological special examination at the end of the term, he had not even procured the books to read on the subject. One day I hypnotized him, and told him while he was asleep that the next day he would begin to work at nine o'clock in the morning, and would continue his labours from nine till one, or at least four hours every morning and two hours every evening. On awaking he remembered absolutely nothing, either of this suggestion or of other experiments which I made during his hypnosis. Next morning he was early astir, buying books, paper, etc., and settled down to work at nine o'clock. He had promised two friends to accompany them to Newmarket that morning, and they accordingly came to fetch him; but he absolutely refused to go and resisted all persuasion. I had him watched by a friend who lived in the same house, and it was quite curious to observe how accurately the suggestion was obeyed.   He would sometimes break off work in the middle of the morning to play the piano or rest, but he always on these occasions exactly fulfilled his four hours of work, so far as our observations went.   On two occasions he went out to dances, not returning until twelve, but each time on reaching home it struck him that he might do a little work before going to bed, and he religiously completed his two hours.   I am glad to say he passed his examination at the end of the term.

Now, in these two cases we have a new phenomenon. We saw before that the sleeping consciousness and the waking consciousness differed as to the matter of their memory chains; but here we find that a command, given during sleep and apprehended only by the sleeping consciousness, is carried out during the waking state, and this notwithstanding that the subject is utterly unaware that any command has been given.   Here, then, we begin to see that the sleeping consciousness may affect us even when we are wide awake, and, if we examine closely, we find that the result of such experiments is usually simply the creation of a desire or impulse to perform the suggested action, a desire of whose origin the subject is completely ignorant.   In the first experiment the impulse to turn on the light was produced; but the patient did not know that it was originated in a command from myself, and hesitated to carry it out directly.   Her question was clearly a subterfuge by which she hoped to satisfy her desire without transgressing the rules of politeness.

(c) *Intellectual Activities of the Sub-consciousness.*— Let us now consider another experiment. During the May week of 1886 I hypnotized G., an undergraduate, one evening, and told him that he would bring me a poem of three stanzas on the May races, on the following evening at nine o'clock. On awakening he did not recollect the suggestion, or any of the occurrences of his sleep. Next day he came to luncheon with me. I hypnotized him again, and he fell at once into a deep somnambulism. I now asked him what I had told him to do, and he answered that he was to write a poem and bring it to me at nine o'clock that evening. I asked whether he had composed any of it, and he said he had made the first verse. This, he said, was as follows :

" Oh, Trinity, Pembroke, John's, Caius,
   Soon, soon in your shoes shall you shiver ;
  You may swagger as much as you please,
  But the Hall will be head of the river."

Not very brilliant poetry, perhaps ! However, on awaking he knew nothing of what had been said, but at nine o'clock he brought me the whole poem of three verses, the first being that given above. He told me that at half-past eight he had suddenly been seized with the idea that he would write a few verses on the May races, and sat down to do so. He said he had written them straight out as they came into his head, seemed rather pleased with his performance,

2

and was evidently disappointed when I told him that I did not think much of them.

Here we have the verses composed in obedience to a suggestion addressed to the secondary consciousness, and without the knowledge of the waking consciousness. The last two verses, at any rate, and possibly the first, were composed during hours of wakefulness, and yet unconsciously in the ordinary acceptation of the term. The secondary consciousness, then, appears to be capable of intellectual activity, and this activity may occur while the person concerned is wide awake, though, of course, quite unaware of these processes.

I have given the above experiments out of many hundreds, because they are in themselves so simple and so easily carried out. The reader will not find it difficult to make successful experiments on similar lines.

So far as we have gone, we see that in somnambulism it is only the waking consciousness which is in suspension. The activity of the sub-consciousness persists during both the waking and the somnambulic states, so that some believe that it never sleeps nor rests, but is always active.

We may now turn to evidence other than that derived simply from hypnotic experiments.

(d) *Motor Automatisms* (the Planchette and Automatic Writing).—Most people have heard of a toy called a planchette. It consists merely of a heart-shaped board, about 8 by 10 inches, with two wheels as supports, the third support being a pencil firmly fixed in a hole in the board. The planchette is placed with the pencil resting on a sheet of paper, and the operator lays one or both hands gently upon it, asking it a question. If the experiment succeeds, the planchette now begins to move in obedience to unconscious pressure, and writes an answer. The important point to notice is that in many cases the experimenter may be utterly unaware of what he has written, and the answer may mention facts of which he believes himself ignorant.

A still simpler plan bids the operator hold a pencil in his hand and rest it lightly on a sheet of paper. In answer to a question, the hand will then move independently of his will, and, as with the planchette, write a message the contents of which may be entirely unknown to him until he has read it. Only certain persons have the power of thus writing automatically, as it is called, but the proportion is quite large.

To return for a moment to the hypnotized subject in the state of somnambulism. Though on awakening he will have completely forgotten all the events of his sleep, yet if he be one of those who can write automatically, when his hand is placed on a planchette or provided with a pencil, and suitable questions are asked, the intelligence that governs the automatic writing will give answers which show that it is cognizant of all that took place during that sleep. For example, I hypnotized G., and during somnambulism I made him imagine that he was (1) riding with the hounds ; (2) rowing a race in his college boat

(3) that next morning he would put a boot on one foot and a shoe on the other. On waking he remembered none of these things. I then made him put his hand on a planchette, and asked, "What did you do first?" After a few meaningless scratches it wrote "Hunting." "What then?" I asked. "Rowed in the races," was the answer. "Did I tell you to do anything?" "Boot one, shoe one," said the planchette. But this particular experiment is so easy to make that I need not multiply examples.

In making experiments of this kind I was struck with one outstanding fact. The knowledge possessed by the planchette was exactly commensurate with that possessed by the subject during somnambulism. The sub-consciousness is therefore identical with the consciousness of the hypnotic sleep, and from this experiment we see that it can carry out actions without collusion of the waking or primary consciousness even when the subject is wide awake. That is to say, both the primary and the secondary consciousness may be acting independently, causing muscular movements at the same moment of time.

The following case strikingly reveals the action of the sub-conscious memory, and incidentally shows that the planchette may be of real use as a means of diagnosis. A gentleman, aged thirty, came to consult me concerning the following history. For nine years he had been oppressed by an indefinable dread of some terrible calamity. He had no idea what it was that he apprehended. For the first two or three years he had managed to control this terror, but after a rather severe attack of influenza it increased greatly, until it became a constant horror, which never left him during his waking hours. His own medical attendant, the only person to whom he had confided his trouble, had died about six months before he came to me, and, perhaps because he had since then kept his condition of mind to himself, the obsession had increased to an extent which threatened to drive him to suicide. I saw him several times and tried hypnotism ; but, though he was susceptible, I was unable to induce somnambulism, and suggestions seemed to have no effect on his dread. One day it struck me that I might find out the cause of his terror by automatic writing. He could, he thought, write with a planchette—at least he had once done so. I got a planchette, made him put his hand upon it, and asked : " Planchette, what is it that frightens him ?" After a few moments the planchette made some scratches. I then said : " Don't make scratches; write an answer." After about half a minute's pause the planchette wrote : " Father's death." I did not let him see what he had written, but substituted a fresh sheet of paper, asking : " Why does that frighten him ?" " Will die the same," was the reply. On inquiry I found that his father had died suddenly of pulmonary embolism, and that my patient, then a child of twelve, had witnessed the death-agony with great horror. This, then, was the cause of panic for which I had so vainly sought. I now tried direct suggestions against the possibility of his dying in this way, and in less than three weeks the old terror had left him. It is worth noticing that even when I made suggestions against this particular idea, he remained quite sceptical as to his having any such notion whatever. He certainly had no conscious idea of the kind.

It is interesting to observe that one may sometimes get quite startling revivals of memory exhibited in automatic writing. I once compelled L., an undergraduate, to write automatically by the simple suggestion "Write." He immediately began writing, and covered sheet after sheet, without being in the least aware of what he had written. On examination I found that much of the matter was a revelation of secrets which he would not willingly have shared with anyone, so I was obliged to let him read the papers and give me such parts as he cared to show. But the remarkable point was that there were a few sentences in a language of which neither he nor I knew anything. I eventually found that it was old Spanish, and the explanation seems to be that in his childhood he used often to examine books in his father's library, and that some of these were written in old Spanish. Doubtless some of the sentences which he had read without understanding were retained in his sub-conscious memory, and reproduced under the influence of the suggestion "Write."

Automatic writing is an instance of what Myers called *motor automatism*—that is, of apparently automatic action really originating in the secondary consciousness. There are, of course, other forms of motor automatism, such as the table-tilting and turning of the spiritualists, and, one may add, certain automatic movements in some cases of hysteria. Motor automatism may also occur quite spontaneously. Thus, a lady was just going to throw certain papers into the fire when she suddenly found her hand arrested. On looking down she saw that among the papers were some five-pound notes. She had doubtless unconsciously noticed them, and the impulse which prevented her from sacrificing them originated in her secondary consciousness.

(e) *Sensory Automatisms.*—But besides manifesting itself by automatic movements, the secondary consciousness is capable of producing sensory phenomena as well.

The most striking instance of sensory automatism, apart from hypnotism, is to be found in what has been termed crystal-gazing, a process much in vogue with spiritualists, who believe that the visions which they see are due to the influence of departed spirits.

The experimenter simply gazes into a glass ball, or glass of water, or some similar object, in the expectation of seeing visions ; and, if he is successful, he soon sees pictures of various kinds in the crystal. A large number of people can do this, and it is perhaps mainly to these forms of motor and sensory automatism that modern spiritualism owes its strength.

These crystal visions may occur quite unexpectedly. A short time ago I was trying to hypnotize a lady, and made her look for a few moments at a cut-glass crystal held above her eyes. Almost at once she exclaimed: "Oh! I see a dog. It is turning round; it is running away." This was succeeded by the appearance of a nurse wheeling a perambulator, and this again by a horse in a dog-cart. I gave up trying to hypnotize her by this method.

The tendency for apparently unnoticed facts to be reproduced by automatism is not uncommon. Miss Z., a well-known crystal-gazer, was one morning looking into her crystal, when she was startled to see in it the printed announcement of the death of a friend. She immediately went to look at a newspaper, and there she found the identical announcement. But she had previously glanced at the column of deaths, though she had not consciously noticed the paragraph in question.

These sub-conscious impressions may also be reproduced in dreams. Mr. C., a friend of mine, while in town lost a cigarette-case which he valued very highly. That night he dreamt that he was at a meeting at the L.C.C. offices (he had really been there that day), and in his dream he heard something fall. Looking down, he saw his cigarette-case. Next morning he got up early, went to the room where the meeting had been held, and found the cigarette-case exactly as he had seen it in his dream.

(*f*) *Passive Attention.*—One factor, concentration of attention, even in ordinary life induces a tendency to a splitting of consciousness,

Thus a man, walking along the street engrossed in conversation, will avoid colliding with other people' though he may not consciously notice them, and may every now and then be so much absorbed in conversing as to be quite unaware that he is avoiding them at all. He is doing two things at once. Of one, the conversation, he is fully aware ; of the other, avoiding passers-by, he is only partially and sometimes scarcely at all conscious. ' These unaware actions are governed by a part of consciousness which has begun to split off from the rest. The condition is sometimes termed one of passive attention.

I suppose that this splitting of consciousness when our attention is fully engaged is a kind of defensive mechanism, which guards us from injuries which we do not avoid consciously when mental interest is otherwise absorbed.

As will be seen in the next chapter, the methods for inducing hypnosis, which after all is a condition of split consciousness, depend upon this limitation of the field of consciousness by concentration of attention.

_(g) *Multiple Personalities.*—I shall not attempt to deal with the questions involved in those rare cases in which the consciousness is liable to apparent disruption into one or more distinct personalities, such as in the well-known case of Sally Beauchamp. They are purely pathological, and, though the phenomena of the secondary consciousness do in a 'measure help to elucidate them, the explanation is still far from being fully understood, and is quite beyond the scope of this little book.

II. Relation of Primary and Secondary Consciousness.

(a) *Nature of the Relationship.*—It has been contended by some that the primary and the secondary consciousness are really completely separate entities, properly designated by the term "personalities." But if we look more closely, we shall, I think, conclude that here—as, indeed, everywhere in Nature—there is no sharp line of demarcation. If we examine the condition of the memory of a subject for events occurring in the different stages of hypnosis, we shall find that as he nears the somnambulistic stage such memory is imperfect, and often very imperfect. Whilst he recollects some occurrences, he forgets others happening apparently in the same stage, though he can generally, but not always, recall these events if reminded of them. The condition of the memory between the waking and sleeping states appears to be one of extremely variable equilibrium, oscillating constantly, tending now to the waking, now to the sleeping state. So much is this the case that it is difficult to get constant results in experiments on memory in this middle phase when it begins to approach somnambulism.

On the whole, perhaps, one may regard the range of consciousness as analogous to the solar spectrum.

The waking consciousness might be represented by the red end of the spectrum, the profound somnambulistic consciousness by the violet, and the deepest part, which, we may suppose, is in relation with the visceral functions, by the ultra-violet invisible rays. Clearly, if we examine the red end of the spectrum, and compare it with the violet, we shall find a sharp line of demarcation .between the two, for wé shall have missed out the orange which bridges them. But if we look at the whole spectrum, it is obvious that it is continuous from end to end. And it is just in the middle part of the hypnotic condition that the conditions of memory are so elusive.

(b) *Its Bearing on Hypnosis.*—We may now briefly consider how the facts in this chapter illuminate the nature of hypnosis. We have seen that the consciousness of the somnambulistic state is the secondary consciousness, and we may infer from the fact that on awaking the subject has no memory of the events of his somnambulism that the activity of the primary consciousness is in suspension during the deep sleep. But we have seen that during the waking state the secondary consciousness is still active, and from the fact that during somnambulism the events of the waking life are remembered, we may infer that all suggestions given in the waking state reach the secondary as well as the primary consciousness. It is clear that in somnambulism we can examine the characteristics of the secondary consciousness in a state of complete detachment from the primary. Unfortu-

nately, we cannot examine the primary consciousness
in a similar condition of isolation, since, as we have
seen, even in the waking state the secondary consciousness is still sufficiently alert to be receptive. If we
compare the normal with the somnambulistic state,
we find that the most striking. point of contrast is
the difference in the degrees of suggestibility. The
most evident characteristic of the latter state is its
enormously *increased suggestibility*, which at once
reaches the maximum degree of which the subject is
susceptible. Nearly every suggestion is immediately
accepted, and each idea so generated seems to be
translated automatically into action. In fact, during
somnambulism nearly every suggested idea gives rise
with almost mechanical certainty to the corresponding
cerebral reflex.

Yet while nearly every suggestion, whether it be
inhibitory or imperative, or even if it be a suggestion
of hallucination, is effective, occasionally some suggestion may fail to act even in somnambulism. It appears
that, as a rule, the function of criticism, though not
extinct during somnambulism, is practically quiescent.
Before it can be called into action there is, one may
suppose, far more inertia to be overcome than in the
normal state. But if the suggestion happens to run
counter to some latent but more powerful idea or suggestion already dominating the field, it may be refused;
and often no amount of insistence can prevail over the
denial. However, whatever the cause may be, it is
certain that the power of criticism as shown by the

rejection of a suggestion is rarely exercised in somnambulism.

The most striking result of the return to the normal state is the constant exercise of the power of criticism. Not every idea is now translated into action. The various suggestions are sifted by the primary consciousness, and only a few are chosen, and allowed to act. The rest are rejected—in other words, their action is inhibited.

The power of criticism and subsequent inhibition appears to be a function of the primary consciousness alone, and so long as consciousness works as a whole, acts throughout. When, however, as in hypnosis, the consciousness is more or less split, the inhibition exercised by the primary consciousness no longer acts fully on the now separated sub-consciousness, and the latter appears to have little or no power of criticism. In deep hypnosis, when the waking consciousness is for the time practically in abeyance, the subject possesses no power of criticism at all.

To this fact is due the increased suggestibility of the hypnotic state. When we make suggestions to a hypnotized subject we are in reality taking a somewhat mean advantage of the fact that his split-off sub-consciousness, in consequence of its lack of the power of criticism, is defenceless.

The condition of total abeyance coexistent with somnambulism is merely the completion of a process of gradual suppression. It commences at the very beginning of the lightest stage of hypnosis. The initiatory suspension of the primary consciousness shows itself in the very earliest condition of hypnosis as a mere disinclination to act in opposition to a suggestion. The subject can successfully resist if he. tries, and, if induced to try by repeated challenges, will do so. Thus, if told that he cannot open his eyes, he makes no attempt to open them; but, if repeatedly defied, he may eventually rouse himself sufficiently to make the attempt, and will succeed. If asked why he did not open them at first, he will say simply that he did not wish to—felt, indeed, a strong disinclination to try. At a slightly more advanced stage he really feels that he cannot even try.

An amusing instance of this condition was afforded by an undergraduate, M. I had on a previous occasion lightly hypnotized him, and one afternoon happened to meet him in the rooms of a common friend. He was standing on the hearthrug, and, soon after I entered, said he must leave, as it was time for him to go to his coach. "But," I said, "you can't go. You can't get off the hearthrug." He laughed and protested that he could, but did not do so, and after a minute or two appealed to me to let him go, else he would get into trouble with his coach. I pointed out that he had just said that he could walk away, and asked why he did not do so if he desired. "Oh yes," he replied, "I could do it if I tried, but I can't try." This condition indicates a slightly more advanced stage in the "disaggregation" of consciousness, as it has been termed.

However, the various stages will be considered more in detail in a later chapter.

The more completely the primary consciousness is suppressed, the more does suggestibility increase. In hypnotism suggestions do not act through the primary or waking consciousness; it is to the sub-consciousness alone that they successfully appeal. Obviously the more the secondary consciousness is liberated from the inhibitory control of the primary consciousness, the more suggestible does the subject become. The final result, when the process of suppression is complete, is, of course, amnesia.

The power of hypnosis, then, resides in the suppression, partial or complete, of the inhibitory rule of the waking or primary consciousness over the dissociated sub-consciousness.

CHAPTER III

METHODS OF THE INDUCTION OF HYPNOSIS

Introductory—Test suggestions—Manner of conveying suggestions (Emphatic *v.* persuasive mode—Personality of operator—Susceptibility of subjects)—Conditions of suggestibility—Processes of induction (Physical methods—Method of Nancy School—Personal method)—Necessity of test suggestions—Method of Dr. Taplin—Allied forms of treatment (Dubois' method — Dr. Bramwell's method) — Awakening of the subject.

A KNOWLEDGE of the methods of inducing hypnosis is, of course, of great importance from the practical standpoint. To the mind of the beginner the actual induction of the hypnotic state often appears a formidable undertaking, encompassed with apparently insurmountable, though really imaginary, difficulties. The very simplicity of the processes employed creates in him a feeling that there really must be something more behind them than he sees or reads of ; and, too, often without even a trial, he concludes that he, at any rate, could never hypnotize anyone, whatever others can do. At heart, in fact, he feels that the successful hypnotist does his work by virtue of some peculiar and incommunicable gift.

But, if the principles which underlie the methods

are once grasped, the difficulty of inducing hypnosis
will be found very slight, and, in the case of good
subjects, absolutely non-existent; while with less
amenable patients this comprehension will enable
even the beginner to vary his devices to an extent
limited only by his inventive ingenuity, so that
probably, even with little practice, he will be able
to hypnotize anyone who is capable of being hypnotized at all.

I. Test Suggestions.

The aim of all the methods is the same—to induce
a condition in which the subject shall be partly or
wholly incapable of resisting suggestions. When the
attempt to produce this condition has been made, the
only criterion of the result is the success or failure of
some definite suggestion. Before making the effort,
therefore, it is necessary to decide clearly what the
first suggestion shall be; and this is a question of
real importance, for we must choose such a one as
is not likely to fail. Upon its consequences very
much will depend, since, after the first suggestion
has been given, the degree of suggestibility in the
patient is markedly altered. Should he respond to it,
his suggestibility is increased, sometimes enormously
increased. If it be ineffectual, his suggestibility is
diminished, sometimes so gravely that hypnotization
by the operator who has failed becomes almost
impossible, while the chances of success even for

others are seriously prejudiced. The very fact that a suggestion has captured the subject leaves a general impression on his mind quite apart from that involved with the nature of the particular suggestion. It creates or helps to strengthen an expectancy that other suggestions will be also irresistible, or at least very difficult to resist, and this mental attitude of itself may undoubtedly deepen the hypnotic state. The sense of frustration and discouragement consequent on the failure of a suggestion, on the other hand, naturally develops into an impression exactly the reverse of this.

The phenomena of suggestion found by experience to be most readily produced are as follows :

1. A sense of quietude and repose.

2. A sensation of warmth on some part of the body on which the operator lays his hand.

3. A feeling of somnolence.

4. A sensation of heaviness of the lids; inability to prevent closure of the eyes.

5. Inability to open the eyes when closed by the previous suggestion.

6. Inability to open the eyes when they have been voluntarily closed.

I have given them roughly in the order of facility from the operator's point of view. In some subjects number three can be induced more readily than number two.

It will be observed that number one is a rather indefinite kind of suggestion, and that the suggestions become more precise according to their place in the sequence.

As aids in deepening the hypnotic state, the earlier suggestions are decidedly less effective than the later ones. Thus, a suggested feeling of quietness and repose, though it indeed makes the subject more susceptible, does so only in a comparatively slight degree. The definite feeling of warmth undoubtedly produces a greater hypnotic result, while the closure of the eyes, with inability to open them, brings about a marked increase of suggestibility. So that it unfortunately happens that the easier the suggestion is to enforce the less hypnotic effect it has, the reason being that these various phenomena belong really to different stages of the hypnotic state, the first to the earlier and those subsequent to the later stages. Our aim is to evoke a phenomenon connected with as deep a condition as we can reach.

II. Manner of Conveying Suggestions.

We have now to consider the best manner of conveying the suggestions. Are they to be given in a commanding voice, with as much emphasis as possible, or are they to be spoken quietly and persuasively?

The chief factors in the strength of a suggestion are, I think—

1. Emphasis and commanding tone.
2. Repetition, which greatly increases the effect.
3. The personality of the operator.

The emphatic and the quiet methods of giving suggestions have each certain advantages and disadvantages.

1 and 2. *Comparison of the Emphatic Mode with the Repetitive Mode.*—An emphatic suggestion is liable to cause a conscious, or at any rate partly conscious, resistance on the part of the subject, and resistance may make hypnotization very difficult. Not infrequently it awakens a deliberate conflict of will.

Again, it cannot be continuously repeated without losing all its force, so that in using a strong suggestion for the first trial one is, so to speak, carrying all one's eggs in one basket. The suggestion once given, success or failure must follow immediately, and failure is certainly likelier than with the gradual methods. On the other hand, if it be effective, and especially if it be effective in spite of an effort at resistance, it has a far more decided and instantaneous victory than any milder suggestion can have.

Young people from about twelve to twenty-two years of age are very susceptible to strong suggestions; and the uneducated classes, even in later life, are equally so. If time is of great importance, and the patient belongs to one of those two classes, it may be worth while to try suggestion in the more commanding form. The most suitable phenomenon to induce in this way is, I think, inability to open the eyes. I often give this as a first suggestion to my patients when they are young or of the hospital class, and, though it does not invariably take effect, the proportion of successes far outnumbers the failures.

On the whole, however, I do not recommend this method to any novice; it takes a certain amount of confidence, and it is perhaps as well to defer it until that has been acquired. When given without any great emphasis, on the other hand, a suggestion may be repeated again and again, not only without loss but with actual gain in power. It becomes a persuasion rather than a command, and should arouse no conscious resistance whatever. The power which it forgoes by the absence of emphasis may be more than compensated for by that accumulated in repetition. In practice this mild and persistent method has the disadvantage that a considerable time may elapse before any marked degree of hypnosis is attained. It may demand many sittings. Each of the six suggestions may be enforced in their order. When number one is successful, number two may be tried, and so on, until at last we succeed with all six, and the subject cannot open his eyes when they have been sealed by suggestion.

Comparing the two methods, we see that the advantage of the strong and emphatic mode is the rapidity with which it acts, the disadvantage being its uncertainty. On the contrary, the more gradual way of giving suggestions persuasively, and increasing their effect by frequent repetition, is comparatively very slow, but very sure.

I suppose, if it were always possible to choose, the

slow method would invariably be, regarded as pre-
ferable to the rapid one; but in actual medical
practice the choice not infrequently lies between immediate hypnosis on the very first sitting or not at
all. Many patients will not contentedly undergo a
number of sittings with no evident hypnotic effect.
They expect immediate results; and I have sometimes had patients sent to me who have been led to
believe by their medical men that one sitting is
enough to induce the condition. Some patients come
up to town for a day to discover whether they are
suitable subjects for hypnotic treatment, and regard
the first trial as conclusively settling the point.
Certainly in these cases it is wiser generally to
decline to attempt treatment under such conditions,
but many circumstances may make refusal almost
impossible.

I do not think that anyone who has successfully
attempted to seal the patient's eyes by a single
emphatic suggestion is ever likely to abandon this
method entirely, on account of the great economy of
time and the power it has of instantly increasing the
suggestibility of the subject, while the extreme pre-
cision with which the whole process can be carried
out is eminently satisfactory.

3. *The Personality of the Operator.*—The stronger
a suggestion the more readily does the subject
respond, so that, granted a fixed degree of suggestibility, the subject may answer to a strong suggestion,
and yet be quite unaffected by the same suggestion if

it be weakly conveyed. The strength of a suggestion may vary enormously. It depends largely upon the tone of voice in which it is given, the gestures accompanying it, and the personality, dominating or otherwise, of the operator. It is natural, therefore, that some persons should be much more successful than others in enforcing obedience to their suggestions. Those who can impress their subjects most readily will be the best hypnotists. A naturally commanding though tolerant temper, considerable human sympathy, and as much knowledge as possible of psychology in the widest sense of the word, are qualities which will greatly strengthen the worker in treatment by suggestion.

All persons are, of course, not equally susceptible to hypnotism. Of healthy persons, however, over 90 per cent. are probably more or less susceptible. But when we use hypnotism for therapeutical purposes we are not dealing with healthy normal subjects : unfortunately, the majority of the nervous disorders which we are called upon to treat by suggestion do of themselves tend to diminish the susceptibility of the patients. Some maladies, it is true, such as dipsomania, seem, if anything, to make their victims more rather than less susceptible. But in a large number of neurasthenics the power of concentration is either entirely gone or very much weakened, or else self-suggestion presents an almost insuperable obstacle. Imbeciles cannot be hypnotized at all, and of lunatics all but a very small proportion appear to be unimpressionable. Bramwell states that out of the first hundred patients he had in London only twenty-two were completely refractory. Thirty-six passed into light hypnosis, thirteen into deep hypnosis, and twenty-nine into somnambulism.

Sex seems to make no material difference to susceptibility; nor, apparently, according to Bramwell and Liébeault, does age. Children from three years of age and upwards are readily influenced. The youngest patient I have had was five years old, and he was readily hypnotized; while Bramwell records a successful case in a child of three.

III. Conditions of Suggestibility.

But with the vast majority of people we must employ some preliminary method of rendering them suggestible at all. Very few are sufficiently suggestible in their normal condition. I do not think that we can do better than recall the conditions enumerated by Sidis as tending to induce hypnosis. I give them again here :

1. Fixation of attention.
2. Monotony.
3. Limitation of muscular movements.
4. Limitation of consciousness.
5. Inhibition.

1 and 4. The really important condition here is clearly the *limitation of consciousness*, the others being obviously subservient to that end. The sub-

ject's attention must not wander at will, but must be as far as possible confined to one idea or set of ideas. Thus, he may be made to think of sleep, with its associated notions of heaviness of the limbs, drowsy feelings, and gradual sealing of the various channels of sense.

As was pointed out in a previous chapter, limitation of the field of consciousness by concentration always tends to create a split in consciousness. The condition of hypnosis being one of dissociation, concentration of attention is the readiest means of bringing it about.

2. Sometimes a subject may become hypnotized in a few moments ; if not, the second condition, that of *monotony*, must be remembered. The process, whatever it is, must be monotonous. Sidis monotonously strokes the subject's forehead, repeating, " Sleep, sleep, sleep," in a level tone of voice, until the patient is subdued to the hypnotic state.

3. I need not emphasize the evident necessity of the *absence of voluntary muscular movements*. A conscious slackening of all the muscles is desirable in the subject, as it seems to be paralleled by a helpful degree of psychical relaxation.

5. The last condition, *inhibition*, or the prevention of the intrusion of foreign ideas, is, of course, essential to the limitation of consciousness. In most of those cases that entirely defy hypnosis the absence of this inhibition is by far the commonest cause of failure. It seems certain that these conditions do conduce to

some measure of suspension of the powers of the
waking consciousness; in other words, to the induction of hypnosis, whether of the lightest or the most
profound kind. I do not for one moment wish the
reader to suppose that the value of the statement of
these conditions is necessarily more than empirical;
they seem, however, to indicate the factors which are
common to all the known methods, though we really
do not know in what their virtue resides. Perhaps
it is not too much to hope that some more certain
process of hypnotic induction may one day be discovered. Possibly some drug may be found to induce
the requisite mental change. Many have already been
tried, and with occasional success, but the drug or
method which will invariably succeed still remains
unknown. Meanwhile we shall see that in all the
various methods used at the present time these conditions do really seem to play a part.

IV. Processes of Inducing Hypnosis.

1. *Physical Methods.*—The actual processes generally recognized—the classical methods, we may term
them—are mainly two: prolonged gazing by the
subject at some small object (Braid's method), and
the use of passes, or long, slow movements of the
operator's hands near to, or in actual contact with,
the body of the subject. But the more one sees of
hypnotism, the more one is convinced that the real
value of these processes consists in the evocation of
Sidis's conditions—viz., fixation of the attention, and

limitation of consciousness, and to the suggestion which
they convey, often vague indeed, but still a suggestion, that the patient in some sense or other is
being subdued to the influence of the operator.

But many other apparently trifling matters may
originate this notion quite strongly. Thus, if the
patient be told to lie down and to make his mind
as blank as possible, or to sit down and try to think
of nothing and to slacken all his muscles, or if he be
merely asked to lie down, shut his eyes, and keep
them shut, each and all of these apparently quite
insignificant actions ought, I am convinced, to be
regarded as real hypnotic processes, which are often
quite as effectual as the better recognized methods of
gazing and passes. The essential point of value in
each case is the quickening of the patient's knowledge
that an attempt is being made, or is about to be made,
to influence him, and it is this knowledge which gives
to the simplest procedures their great significance.

While I am not prepared to deny that prolonged
gazing at some small object and the use of passes
may have some other intrinsic power to produce the
hypnotic state, I am sure that their power of doing
so has been greatly exaggerated, though to the un-
practised hypnotist they do, I believe, have some
value, for they tend to impart to the operator a
certain confidence, and a suggestion given with confidence, which it is difficult to simulate, is in itself
a very real power. As means of emphasizing a
suggestion, both passes and gazing are undoubtedly

useful. The steady, concentrated gaze of the operator can also impress a subject to an extraordinary extent. Even without any other preliminary process, a determined gaze often compels obedience to a suggestion. When at Cambridge, I frequently used this method when I was collecting subjects for the purpose of experiment. On more than one occasion I tried standing before a number of undergraduates and simply asking them to look at my eyes. Then I gazed steadily at whom I considered the best subject, suggesting that he must get up from his chair and come to me. In a minute or so, notwithstanding his resistance, he had to obey. Then, by a similar treatment of the others present, I on one occasion compelled no fewer than eleven out of thirteen to obey the suggestion and approach me. None of these had been hypnotized before.

I mention this experiment to show that merely witnessing the hypnotization of others does of itself increase the suggestibility of a prospective subject, and must be included under the general definition as a hypnotic process, since it is, I believe, the most powerful and unfailing method of breaking down the resistance of a subject. It was on this principle that Wetterstrand relied in hypnotizing his patients, and to it his astonishing percentage of successes must be regarded as mainly due. His fresh patients were present while his old were hypnotized, and the impression made was overpowering, so that he practically never failed to affect them at the first trial.

But for practical purposes, when we have to hypnotize subjects singly, and not in groups, as Wetterstrand did, the one essential factor in rendering the subject suggestible is suggestion itself. The beginner must clearly grasp one point—*viz.*, that without an accompanying command or persuasion, either verbally given or tacitly understood by the patient, no process of any kind is likely to be of the slightest avail in producing the desired hypnotic state.

Almost all the older investigators, and many of the modern ones, have apparently resorted in the first instance to physical devices. Mesmer invented and used a number, all equally successful, because, of course, behind them all lay the great, and then unknown, power of suggestion. Braid, when he first began to hypnotize, used to make patients gaze for a long time at some small bright object, held slightly above the eyes, about a foot distant, at the same time telling them to look steadily at it, and to concentrate their attention on it. Sometimes the eyes after a time would close spontaneously; if not, he repeated the process, instructing the patient to allow his eyes to close when the operator brought his two extended fingers towards them, and, after his lids were shut, still to direct his eyeballs towards the object, trying to picture it, and keeping his attention riveted on it. Usually this process succeeded; and it is worth noting that it is as a rule harder for a patient to open his eyes when the eyeballs are kept in such a position. Later, however, Braid recognized that verbal suggestion was the best method of inducing hypnosis, and stated his belief that anyone who could be hypnotized at all could be hypnotized by its means without any recourse to physical methods. With regard to this prolonged gazing, as originally advocated by Braid, it is interesting to note that sometimes, even in children who cannot by any possibility know what is expected, it may produce deep hypnosis, without any suggestion of any kind. It is just possible that the feeling of heaviness produced by the process may of itself suggest sleep, and, of course, the monotony and fixation of attention may be expected to induce some degree of hypnosis. But I do not think this method is suited for purposes of medical treatment. It is tedious and exhausting to the patient, and, as it absorbs more time than more direct methods, it has nothing to recommend it in preference to them.

Among the public hypnotists who perform on the stage a modification of Braid's method is often used. Madam Card, who was, I think, one of the most successful, used to seat her subjects on the stage, placing in the hand of each a metal disc, at which he was directed to gaze. After about ten minutes, which she occupied by talking to the audience, she went to each in turn, and, taking away his disc, told him to look at her eyes. She stared at him fixedly for half a minute or so, at the same time stroking his forehead and brows with rather rapid strokes, and then bade him close his eyes. Finally, placing her hand on his forehead, and pressing strongly against it, she said:

"Your eyes are fast; you cannot open them—it is impossible." If she achieved her end with the first two or three, she was generally successful with most of the others. If she failed with the first few, the failure generally acted as a strong counter-suggestion, and she would then frequently fail with all the rest. Her power undoubtedly lay in the extraordinary intensity of expression which she could throw into her gaze. She literally glared her subjects into submission.

2. *Method of the Nancy School.*—But for practical purposes there is absolutely no necessity to resort to physical methods at all. With limitation of consciousness, suggestion alone, either rapidly or gradually enforced, is the real power which induces hypnosis. Such devices, for instance, as the use of a revolving mirror for the patient to gaze at, as advocated by Luys, will, I believe, hypnotize no one who cannot be hypnotized by mere suggestion. However, one physical device at least may accelerate the process. Many persons are more readily hypnotized if they are made to extend the head backwards as far as possible while hypnotization is carried out. The reason seems to be that in, this position mental activity is more difficult. I remember one travelling hypnotist who used to take advantage of this. He hypnotized his subject by standing behind the chair on which he was seated, and then, forcibly bending his head backwards, gazed into his eyes for a few moments, closed them, and suggested that they could

not be opened. He was very effective, and I have often succeeded with the same method.

It is to the Nancy School that we are indebted for the modes of inducing hypnosis by pure suggestion, and the methods of Liébeault, Bernheim, and Beaunis, three of its chief leaders, resemble each other very closely.

Liébeault and Bernheim used to place the patient in a chair, and then tell him to look steadily at the operator's eyes. Sometimes the eyes would close spontaneously; but if not, suggestions were made at once. The suggestions of both the operators were very similar. " Your eyelids are getting heavy ; your eyes feel tired ; your limbs feel heavy and numb ; you are getting drowsy. Think of nothing but sleep. Your eyes are closing," etc. In most cases this succeeded immediately.

Beaunis used simply to make the patient gaze steadily at his eyes, and the lids would close in a few moments in successful cases. He gave no verbal suggestion ; but it must be remembered that the inhabitants of Nancy were so familiar with hypnotism and its general results that the patient shared in the common knowledge of the kind of effect which was intended, so that the suggestion that the eyes should close was already in his mind before any attempt at hypnosis was made.

At Nancy everyone had heard of hypnotism and was more or less intimate with it, while immense numbers had been hypnotized, thus creating an attitude of mind which greatly favours the induction of the trance. It is not so in England. Here the majority have heard of hypnotism only as something mysterious and uncanny, or know nothing at all about it, except probably its name ; thus we lack the potent auxiliary which exists in France. Ignorance is certainly a real hindrance. The idea is strange, and the strangeness distracts the patient ; he wonders what will happen, and sometimes cannot refrain from an attempt to analyze his own feelings, a great and often fatal bar to hypnosis. Hence in this country we must take this bewilderment into account, and, if possible, try to familiarize patients with the characteristics of the hypnotic state before we make any effort to influence them.

3. *Personal Method.*—Though I cannot pretend to say what is the best method of inducing hypnosis, for it seems doubtful whether there is any method which can be called the best for all cases, I state a method which I have used for the last six or seven years, and which appears to me to offer two real advantages—viz., extreme rapidity and a very large percentage of successes at the first trial (about 92 per cent).

Like others, I found that one common obstacle to success was more or less conscious resistance on the part of the subject—a resistance which he could not help exerting even when he was anxious to assist.

Most patients find it difficult to aid the operator, and it was with a view of preventing conscious resist-

ance and enlisting the willingness of the subject that
I devised the method.

It is extremely easy, and nearly always induces
a condition of suggestibility within a minute. I rarely
try a patient for more than two minutes, and never
for longer than three.

Before hypnotizing a patient, if he be old enough
to understand, I always tell him that it is important
that he should understand the principles underlying
hypnotism in order that he may be able to help to
render himself suggestible.

I tell him that it depends on the fact that, if we
concentrate our attention on anything with sufficient
intensity, our consciousness always tends to split
in two. As an illustration I use the man walking
along the street engrossed in conversation, which
will be found in the previous chapter.

These unaware actions, I tell him, are governed by a
part of consciousness split off from the rest, and the
split-off part possesses so little power of criticism that
it accepts suggestions quite readily since it cannot see
that they are really absurd.

" So," I tell him, " if you will concentrate your
attention on anything for a short time, and if I then
make any suggestion such as that you cannot take
your hand off mine, you will find that you cannot."

The explanation is quite simple. Whilst your waking
consciousness can criticize the suggestion and say that
it is nonsense, your split-off consciousness, which
exercises a considerable control over your bodily move-

ments, is such a fool that it cannot criticize at all. In effect all it can say is, "Oh, I can't take my hand off yours, can't I? Very well, then, I can't," and you will find that you cannot do it. All suggestion, I tell him, is simply a way of taking advantage of the fact that the split-off consciousness, or sub-consciousness, is such a hopeless fool.

I then always try to remove some common misconceptions about hypnotism.

I tell him that, in hypnosis, however deep, the subject is always completely conscious, and can always hear everything I say, and that, except for the fact that he will be unable to resist suggestions, he will remain exactly as he normally is.

I now make him lie down and relax all his muscles. His hand, if raised and let go, should fall absolutely dead.

I now tell him that I want him to look at a small cut-glass crystal for a few moments, and explain to him that the sole object of this is to give him something on which he can concentrate his attention.

I now say, "Whilst you are looking at it, I want you to blink as much as ever you like; let your eyes get as heavy as ever they can, and let yourself become as drowsy as possible, and do not rouse at all." The whole point of the method lies in these words.

I now hold the piece of cut-glass eight or ten inches away from his eyes and make him concentrate his gaze on it, and at the same time stroke his forehead and repeat once more, "Blink as much as you like," etc.

After ten seconds I say, " Your eyes are getting heavier now ; you are becoming drowsy, they are half closed " ; and I take away the glass and he looks at my eyes instead. After about ten seconds more or less the eyes generally close; and, if not, I tell him to close them, and stroke the lids once or twice.

As a rule I make no suggestion as to the eyes being sealed until I have made the next test, the reason being that, in many of these nervous cases, the stages frequently fail to occur in their normal order.

I stroke both arms, saying they will begin to feel heavy, and then I make him grasp my hand, and pull hard against his grasp. I then stroke his arm and tell him that his hand is becoming fast to mine, and that the more he tries to take it off the harder he will grasp. He tries to take his hand off but cannot. I then seal his eyes, and he is sufficiently susceptible for most therapeutic purposes.

I have given this method in some detail as I have found it so satisfactory. In only a few cases does this procedure fail at first trial, and the failure is usually due to lack of concentration.

Sometimes a patient will find it easier to attend to the monotonous beat of a metronome, or the sound of running water, than the glass of crystal. Another method which I have tried with success in a few obstinate cases is to make the patient breathe, as nearly as he can, once every three seconds, and make him attend to his breathing. I have not tried this method often enough to test it thoroughly ; but from what I have seen. I think it may prove a valuable device.

People who are really musical can often render themselves suggestible by going through a piece of music mentally.

Whereas in former days I did not generally try to hypnotize patients at their first interview, I now practically always do so, and I find that over 90 per cent. are hypnotized to some degree at a first trial.

If, however, the patients be very nervous of hypnotism, I tell them that I will not hypnotize them, but will show them exactly what I shall want them to do when they next come, so that as they will know what is going to happen, they will feel no nervousness on their next visit. Very often they succumb whilst being shown what they are required to do. If not, I make no real attempt at suggestion until, after a few trials, they lose their nervousness.

It is amazing what an immense difference concentration makes. One case which I failed to influence on twenty-two occasions, because he could not fix his attention, succumbed at once when I suggested that he should try to centre his attention on his own home. He could do that, though on previous occasions he had failed altogether to limit his thought to the idea of sleep.

In the case of failure, on the second day, I generally repeat the same process as on the first, and as a rule the eyes close, or at any rate show signs of heaviness. Usually, after the patient has fixed his gaze on some small bright object for a few seconds, I make him fasten his eyes on mine for a short time, repeating again the suggestions as to heaviness, etc. It is quite astonishing how suddenly the steady gaze of the operator will influence a subject. In many it causes an almost immediate closure of the eyes. Now, however, if the eyes show no signs of closing or of heaviness, I think it best to follow Sidis's plan, and tell the subject to close his eyes and confine his mind as far as possible to one set of ideas. I then keep on repeating the suggestion, " Sleep, sleep, sleep," at the same time monotonously stroking his forehead. After a few minutes I generally raise one hand, and very gently let it go again. Often it stays where I have placed it, showing some degree of catalepsy. Even if it does not, I suggest that the patient will find difficulty in opening his eyes, that the limbs are getting heavy, etc. I then inform him that when I tell him to open his eyes he will probably be able to do so, but with more than normal difficulty. When he is told to try, the prediction is nearly always fulfilled. He may be quite unable to open them at all, or only after hesitation. If he remains unaffected, I generally make him shut them again, and resume for a short time, suggesting sleep as before, but I make no more trials on that occasion.

In the case of failure, it is advisable to elicit all one can from the patient, with the view of discovering the cause. This almost invariably proves to be lack of the power of concentration. In that case, when he next comes, I try to find something on which he

thinks he will be able to fix his attention, and, going
through the same kind of process, often succeed. But
there is one factor, self-suggestion, which sometimes
prevents hypnosis, and I know of no method which
will with any certainty overcome this obstacle. These
self-suggesting people furnish most of the really un-
hypnotizable cases. One can only try again on
another occasion, and keep on repeating the attempt
until one either succeeds or concludes that further
efforts are useless.

It is always advisable to get the patient to think of
hypnosis as a gradual process, sometimes satisfactorily
induced only after several sittings. And sometimes
with such subjects as require therapeutic treatment,
it does take several trials to arrive at much effect.
But in the vast majority, even of those who at first
show no sign of hypnosis, repeated trials do succeed,
especially if one can rectify mistakes in the conditions,
such as failure of concentration.

It is worth mentioning that, when an attempt is
made to prevent a subject from opening his eyes,
firm pressure on the forehead seems to intensify the
suggestion considerably.

4. *Necessity of Test Suggestion.*—It is, of course, not
necessary to test the actuality of hypnosis by the
suggestion of closure of the eyes. Many make no
tests, relying simply on the account of the experience
given by the patient when he is aroused, such as the
presence or absence of heaviness or somnolence, and
the feeling of disinclination to move, etc. Personally,

I generally do aim at this one test, as I then feel really satisfied that the subject is hypnotized to some degree, even if it be only very slightly; but others try to produce a feeling of warmth by laying the hand on the patient's body and suggesting the sensation of a warm glow beneath it. I do not think it much matters what test is applied, so long as it is a criterion that will show the existence of quite light degrees of hypnosis, and does not exact an advanced stage for its success. Testing the presence of hypnosis by an experimental suggestion has one other advantage besides the reassurance of the operator. If effectual, the suggestion will increase suggestibility, and on this ground also it seems to me advisable.

5. *Method of Dr. Betts Taplin.*—Some prefer slower methods as being the most certain. Thus Dr. Betts Taplin, of Liverpool, who, I believe, rarely fails to hypnotize his patients, does so by very gradual methods. On the first day he simply talks to his patient, explaining the nature of the treatment. On the next he sometimes merely makes the patient lie down, and suggests a feeling of rest and quietude. On the next he suggests the sensation of warmth in some part of the body, usually the epigastrium, on which he lays his hand, then heaviness of the eyes, limbs, etc., so that it is only after several sittings that any attempt at closing the eyes can be made. Though very lengthy, this method has the advantage of being more certain than many others, and in his hands it has proved an exceedingly sure one.

● But the beginner, if he will but remember that the chief condition found requisite for the production of hypnosis is limitation of consciousness, and will bear in mind the suggestions which are most readily enforced, must find that the process of induction of hypnosis is far easier than appears at first sight. If he be good at giving really strong suggestions, he will probably generally use the shorter processes ; if not, he will find that he succeeds best with the more gradual methods. Once hypnosis has been induced, it can be deepened in susceptible subjects either by the reiterated command to sleep or by the suggestion of the various phenomena of the different states described in the chapter on the stages of hypnosis. It happens not infrequently that the simple methods above described will of themselves induce deep hypnosis, or even somnambulism, at the first trial, without any further procedure.

6. *Allied Methods of Treatment.*—Other methods of suggestion, without hypnosis, are employed by many, and their advocates claim that the results are as successful as, or even better than, those obtained by hypnotism.

(a) *Dubois' Method.*—The method of Dubois deserves more notice than can be given it here. It is applicable to many kinds of neuroses. He does not hypnotize his patients, but, after a searching diagnosis of the psychical as well as the physical conditions of the case, he tries by reasoning and argument to convince them that they are curable and must get well, and to

induce them constantly to reassure themselves that
their symptoms will vanish. He helps them by
encouraging suggestions every time he sees them.
To me his treatment appears to rely mainly on
suggestions of cure made by the patient to himself,
and the results, which are exceedingly good, seem
to flow from this induced habit of therapeutical self-
suggestion. But the method is inapplicable to some
cases, and must require singular powers of persuasion
in the physician. Dubois objects to hypnotism, and
even falls foul of the term " suggestion "; his method,
he says, acts by persuasion. Still, his work is of
great value in helping to emphasize the necessity of
comprehending the psychical aspect both of nervous
maladies and of their cure.

(b) *Dr. Bramwell's Method.*—Another method, employed by Dr. Bramwell—one which he now uses to
the exclusion of hypnotism—demands some consideration. The patient sits down, and is told to think of
some restful mental picture. The nature of the picture
is unimportant, provided it be one which can hold his
interest. He is instructed not to observe the suggestion given by the physician, and upon his power
of inattention the success of the procedure is said to
depend. Two kinds of suggestion are then made.
The first refers to the conditions which the operator
wishes to create while the patient is in the armchair.
He is told that each time he comes he will find it
easier to rest, to turn his attention away from the
operator, and to concentrate it upon some restful

idea. It has been previously explained to him that the physician's aim is not to produce sleep, but that if he can get into the drowsy condition that precedes sleep, the curative suggestions are likely to find response more quickly.

The other suggestions are curative, and begin with the first treatment. Often the patient is unable on the first occasion to divert his attention from these, but after a few treatments he is generally able to do so, and to form some serene imaginary picture, often passing into a dreamy, drowsy state. Sometimes he lapses into a condition of slight natural sleep. It is difficult to explain the success of this method in the absence of experiments to show how it acts. Bramwell says: "The suggestions given are supposed to reach the secondary consciousness and to call its powers into play "—evidently because the primary consciousness, tricked into preoccupation, leaves the secondary more easily accessible. Probably this is so, since such suggestions have practically no power over the primary consciousness. It is clear that the method is a process in which limitation of consciousness and monotony have a part, so that we may reasonably suppose that some amount of hypnosis may often occur. As Sidis has, I think, satisfactorily proved, in the normal condition only indirect suggestions have appreciable effect, and even then the effect is but slight, whilst in hypnosis the more direct the suggestion the more powerful it is in producing results.

It is unnecessary to point out the great advantage

of a really successful method of enforcing suggestions
without the aid of hypnosis, both as regards economy
of time and also as regards the number of cases which
could be treated by its means; for it would then
make no difference in suggestive treatment whether
the patient were hypnotizable or not, since, after all,
the only object of inducing hypnosis is to render the
subject more suggestible.

But it seems possible that both methods have their
value, and that some cases can be more successfully
treated by one than the other. I have seen, for
instance, a bad case of dipsomania, which had been
treated without the slightest result for some weeks in
a nursing home by suggestion without hypnosis, yield
at once to suggestion under light hypnosis; and yet
I know that the medical man who treated the patient
in the first instance has succeeded in many similar
cases by his method.

I do not advise anyone to restrict himself to one
method, though at first it is doubtless best to practise
with one until it becomes familiar. Eventually he
will be able to judge for himself which methods suit
him best in general, for there can be little doubt that
each worker will discover some one mode of procedure
peculiarly suited to his individuality.

Note on the Awakening of the Subject.

To arouse a subject from the hypnotic sleep the
command to "wake" is all that is necessary. It is,

however, best to arouse him gradually. I generally suggest that he will wake when I have counted ten, and then count slowly aloud.

In only two instances have I known of difficulty in ending the sleep. In both cases the subject had been hypnotized by two different men at a few minutes' interval, and could be awakened by neither. One was finally aroused by having cold water dashed in his face; and the other, who had passed into the imitative stage, was eventually wakened by an ingenious ruse. When I pass over one of my patients to anyone else for treatment, I always suggest in hypnosis that he will obey his new hypnotizer, and wake at his command. This precaution had been omitted in the two instances mentioned.

CHAPTER IV

THE PHENOMENA OF HYPNOSIS—THE STAGES

Introductory statement—Erroneous impressions of hypnosis—
Determination of stages of hypnosis—Detailed account of
stages 1 to 5—Comparison with stages of Liébeault and
Bernheim.

General Statement.

IF a number of subjects are hypnotized, the suggestions to which they respond are not the same in
every case. Thus, in some, closure of the eyes is
the only phenomenon that can be evoked. In others
we may produce, in addition, inability to carry, out
a voluntary movement, such as writing or walking,
though we cannot compel them to initiate such a
voluntary movement. Others, again, will show the
phenomena above mentioned, and will also yield
obedience to some imperative suggestion—for instance,
a command to rise from a seat—though memory
cannot be inhibited, even for single facts.

If we group the sets of phenomena as A, B, C,
etc., and take a large number of subjects, we shall
find that some are capable of showing the phenomena
of group A only; others, again, of group B as well

as of group A; others, again, of groups A, B, and C; and others of groups A, B, C, and D (D representing groups still more advanced).

We may therefore experimentally divide the hypnotic condition into stages, each stage being characterized by its particular group of phenomena. Since, however, it is possible to produce in every stage some at least of the phenomena of all the stages preceding it, we can tell the actual stage of hypnosis which any subject may happen to reach only by ascertaining what are the most advanced phenomena that can be elicited; then, by referring to the group to which they belong, we readily determine the stage of hypnosis which the subject has attained. The different groups of phenomena that become manifest as the subject advances from the lightest to the deepest states of hypnosis can, of course, be determined only by actual experiment with a large number of subjects.

Anyone who intends to make use of hypnotism for therapeutic purposes will, naturally, be better equipped if he has some knowledge of the general course of the phenomena which may be evoked by its means— if he realizes what, in fact, are the stages through which the subject will pass as he goes, by almost imperceptible degrees in many instances, from the lightest possible condition of slightly increased suggestibility to the state of profound somnambulism.

It might be supposed from the name " hypnotism " that the commonest characteristic of the hypnotic state was the hypnotic sleep. As a matter of fact comparatively few subjects reach this particular condition; nor, fortunately, is it necessary for therapeutical purposes, except in a very small number of cases. It is generally held that only about 15 per cent. ever pass into the deep state at all. The great majority, therefore, show only the characteristics of the light or waking state, in which there is no break in the continuity of the memory of the subject. There is another general, but quite erroneous, impression that the hypnotic sleep is a condition of unconsciousness. The subject, even in somnambulism, remains completely conscious, though on awaking he forgets all the experiences of his " sleep." Probably this loss of memory has become confused with the idea of loss of consciousness. Some rare patients do occasionally pass into a condition of lethargy resembling a very heavy normal sleep; but even these subjects, though too inert to respond to spoken suggestions, are probably more or less conscious—certainly not less conscious than in deep natural sleep.

The stages here described were those defined by Professor Langley and myself when experimenting many years ago at Cambridge. These early stages have long become familiar in public exhibitions of hypnotism. Some were mentioned by Braid, and an account of certain of their phenomena, as produced by Lewis and Darling in 1851, is given by Bennett and by Gregory.

The first object of our experiments was to ascertain whether the different stages of the waking state could be arranged in sequence, so that a subject showing the phenomena of any stage (whether earlier or later) in the succession could also be made to show the phenomena of all the stages preceding it.

The subjects were all men, nearly all were under-graduates, and all were in good health. Besides dealing with the subjects on whom Langley and I worked together, I experimented by myself on a large number, and the results, as regards the stages, I found to be always, or very nearly always, the same.

The method of inducing hypnosis which we adopted was very simple. We gazed at the subject from thirty to sixty seconds, generally stroking his temples and forehead at the same time, and making strokes or passes over the top of his head. He was then asked to shut his eyes, over which a few more passes or strokes were generally made; one hand was then laid firmly on his forehead, and the suggestion was given : "You cannot open your eyes." If this succeeded—and it did succeed in the majority of cases—we went on to try other inhibitory suggestions. Thus, in their order, we induced rigidity of the limbs, obedience to imperative suggestions, loss of memory for particular facts, simple delusions, and loss of sensation. After this we attempted to produce illusions. If these were evoked, the subject would usually pass into the deep state. If not, we tried the suggestion, "Sleep."

We found the subjects hypnotized by this method

5

showed no alteration from their normal appearance in the first three and often in the first four stages, therein differing from the subjects of Liébeault and Bernheim, who proceeded on a different plan, obtaining by gazing, passes, and the suggestion of sleep the maximum degree of hypnotization possible. Thus, even their first stage is marked by more or less drowsiness, owing possibly to the reiterated suggestion of sleep, which we never used until we wished to produce the deep state.

With regard to the stages as we differentiated them, two points are to be noted :

1. The stages are not sharply marked off from each other. They are due to a loss of voluntary control over some of the muscular movements of the body, others remaining under that control. But the loss of power has many degrees. It may show itself in a mere slight hesitation in performing the movement affected by the inhibitory suggestion ; or it may, indeed, be utterly impossible for the subject to perform the movement so long as the suggestion is maintained.

It must be understood that the relations of the stages 1, 2, 3, etc., to each other are such that a certain number of subjects show the phenomena of stage 1 only. Others show the phenomena of stages 1 and 2 only ; and when the phenomena of stage 2 or stage 3 can be produced, then those of stage 1 or stages 1 and 2 respectively can also be made apparent.

In most cases, when stage 3 can be produced, then the phenomena of stage 2 appear more readily, and those of stage 1 still more so. Some subjects, however, are so susceptible that it is difficult to discriminate degrees in the ease with which the phenomena of the different stages are evoked, and in some it is easier to produce somnambulism than the phenomena of the waking state without it.

2. If a subject is taken beyond the early stages of hypnotism, so that when at rest his condition is obviously abnormal, and suggestions are then made to him, he cannot afterwards be experimented upon to determine these early stages unless the suggestions given in the deep state have been most carefully noted. For after a suggestion has been successfully made in the deep state, the subject's condition is so altered that the same suggestion given in his waking state is more readily carried out than it was before. The fact makes such experiments difficult unless one can obtain a great range of subjects.

It cannot be claimed that the stages are always exactly the same in all subjects, yet variations are neither remarkable nor frequent. The phenomena depend upon the receptivity of the nervous system, and, since this may be altered in deep hypnosis, we may naturally expect some differences to exist even in healthy persons, and still more in unhealthy persons, especially in those suffering from a perversion of some one or other function of the nervous system. None of our experiments were made upon hysterical subjects, but the different accounts given of the early stages in hysterical patients do not seem surprising;

indeed, their close conformity with those found in healthy people would be much more a matter for wonder.

The stages observed are as follows :

Stage 1.—In this stage the subject can be prevented from carrying out those voluntary movements which are most commonly accomplished in ordinary life by reflex action ; such are those affecting the muscles of the eyes, face, and respiration. The typical movement is that of opening the eyes, and this, of all movements, appears the easiest to prevent. This inhibition has long been the first experiment tried by public performers on the stage, and Liébeault and Bernheim also mention it as one of the easiest phenomena to obtain. Other phenomena belonging to this class are the preventions of shutting the eyes, opening the mouth, swallowing, taking a deep breath, breathing.

Both in this stage and in stage 2 the more commonly the movement is carried out by reflex action and the less commonly by volition, the easier it is to inhibit it by suggestion. It is worth noting in this connection that one act, at any rate—viz., sneezing, which is practically an entirely reflex act—can be prevented in almost anyone, even in the normal states, by a direct inhibitory suggestion. This is also not infrequently the case with regard to micturition, which, however, can generally be prevented only after the first stage has been produced.

According to Heidenhain, in a considerable number

of subjects the only sign of hypnosis that can be obtained is inability to open the eyes, and this accords with my own experience. Of these, he says, some can be prevented from opening the mouth as well. In some, other muscles can be affected—*e.g.*, after a few strokes over a strongly flexed arm the subject may be unable to extend it. He compares this with a condition described by Richet, where a voluntary contraction causes a contracture. Whether he thinks the inability to open the eyes and mouth is caused in this way is not clear. In fact, however, the first obvious sign of hypnosis is the inability of the subject to open his eyes *when told he cannot do so*. This feature may be strongly marked, although it may be quite impossible to produce any contracture in the rest of the muscles. So far as we have observed, a stray voluntary contraction may sometimes aid the effect of suggestion, but does not of itself produce any contracture. I am not here speaking of subjects who have been deeply hypnotized or who are hysterical.

It is important to recognize that hesitation in opening the eyes is as true a sign of commencing hypnosis as the most absolute inability to open the eyes at all. Of course, the subject is more deeply hyp-notized in the latter case, but he is as truly influenced in the former ; and it will almost always be found that by repeating the process, the slight hesitation may be converted, though often only gradually converted, into an absolute disability. It is worth while to draw attention to this point, for by many not familiar with hypnotism a suggestion imperfectly carried out is regarded as a failure, although it unmistakably indicates a certain degree, at any rate, of hypnosis.

Stage 2.—In this stage we find three different classes of phenomena. All subjects in this stage show the phenomena of the first stage, combined with one or more of the phenomena of the second :

(a) The limbs can be made rigid.

(b) After suggestion, the subject is unable to control the movement of his limbs—that is, he can be prevented from voluntarily carrying out movements not included in stage 1.

(a) *Rigidity.*—To produce rigidity, light strokes or passes are made over the limbs of the subject, and he is told his limbs are becoming stiff.   This appears to happen most easily with the hand, then with the arms, then with the legs.   We rarely tried to influence the body muscles.   In almost all these cases passes aid the effect of verbal suggestion.   In some, pointing with the finger seems equally efficacious, and simple suggestion really does as well.   The rigidity produced varies greatly in intensity in different subjects.   It may be so slight that the subject only just appreciates it, or so extreme as to be somewhat painful, and leave a feeling of fatigue.   In general, the more extreme the rigidity, the longer it takes for the subject to relax the muscles after the suggestion has ceased.   In some subjects when, say, the hand has been made rigid, it can be flexed ·almost instantly when an attempt is made to do so. In others the rigidity produced cannot voluntarily be ended within a minute or more. It may require a considerable external force to move the limb, which, when released, flies back to its original position. It must be understood that in these cases no suggestion has been given to the subject that he cannot move a limb. He is simply asked whether he can bend it—his hand, for instance. It is well known the time taken to perform such a movement is decreased by suggestions like "Now you can close your hand." If this alone does not lead to flexion, a few passes over the hand in a direction contrary to those made in stiffening it are often effective. Occasionally the subject still cannot flex his hand. In that case flexion may be produced by the command of the operator to open the hand. When, however, the rigidity does not rapidly disappear, experiment shows that the subject can be made to show more or less markedly the phenomena of stage 3. In some cases we tried plunging the stiffened hand into hot water, which caused the rigor to vanish instantly. Cold water seemed to produce the same effect as hot; but more slowly.

One subject—C.—who was able by self-suggestion to produce great rigidity in any limb, was also able, by thinking of his arm as being relaxed, to prevent to a great extent the production of rigidity by us. All that we could do by suggestion and by passes was to produce a stiffness insufficient to cause any appreciable delay in the voluntary movement. The subject, whose hand was relaxed by hot water, eventually succeeded in making his hand rigid by self-suggestion. He found that he could bend it more quickly when he held it near the fire. Having repeated the experiment several times, he placed his hand on his leg, and then found that as long as he kept his hand in that position he was unable to stiffen it. We also were unable to make his hand rigid, either by suggestion or passes, as long as he kept it in contact with his leg, whereas, if it were removed an inch or so, we could do so instantly. This is interesting, as showing the way in which a suggestion may work. Before he had experienced the rapid reduction effect of hot water, we could make his hand rigid, whether he kept warm or not; but afterwards warmth gave rise to the suggestion of laxness in the muscles to such a degree that neither spoken nor other suggestions of rigidity produced any effect. In most subjects the placing of the hand in hot water rendered it somewhat less easy to reproduce rigidity, but the difference was often very slight. The following case, belonging to a stage later than that here dealt with, shows how hot water may annul the effect produced by passes:

A.'s hands became insensitive under strokes or passes, the loss of sensation beginning at the tips of the fingers, and spreading upwards. He was asked, without being told why, to dip his fingers to about the first joint in hot water. After drying them, he was asked to put his hand through a hole in the screen, so that he could not see his hand or what was done to it. Passes were made over this hand, and it was found that the ends of the fingers retained their sensitiveness, whereas in the rest of the fingers sensation for all except very strong stimuli disappeared.

Squeezing the muscles in some cases markedly increased the strength of contracture. Thus in J., in whom contracture from light stimuli and suggestion is only slight, a strong contracture is produced by squeezing the muscles. With C., in whom contracture is readily obtained by light stimuli, squeezing the muscles produces much greater rigidity, which it takes much longer to remove. Probably the strong stimuli act by increasing the force of the suggestion. It is a question whether contracture of the muscles cannot be produced with an ease which varies inversely with the frequency with which in ordinary life they are used reflexly—that is, without effort of will. Thus, the muscles of the limbs are more easily made rigid than those of the face. When a subject whose hand was rigid tried to bend it, it always appeared, as far as our experience went, that the first and second fingers were the last to be completely flexed. Later experiments on these subjects showed that it took fewer passes to make these two fingers rigid than the third and fourth fingers or the thumb.

It seems clear that the primary change in the

nervous system which produces contracture lies in the cortex of the brain, for in nearly all fresh subjects passes do not produce contracture unless accompanied by verbal suggestion. The change is probably an active and not an inhibitory process. It has been supposed by some that the condition is due to the inhibition of the cortex, the lower centres being so left freer to act; but if this be the case, how is contracture produced by simple suggestion to be explained? It can hardly be supposed that the ordinary stimuli from the skin and organs of the body are sufficient to produce strong rigidity of the muscles of the body, even supposing that the higher centres are not acting. This is not the case in paralysis from injury to the brain, or in cases of injury to the spinal cord. Consequently the contracture is probably produced by an activity of certain parts of the cortex of the brain— that is, caused by the idea of contracture. This disturbance must be restored to quiescence before the contracture can disappear.

In certain prolonged experiments on the hands of subjects, partly through a screen, it has sometimes happened that the arms have become more rigid than the hands. Perhaps this was due partly to reverse strokes being made over the hand, and not over the arm. In other cases we found the arm more readily rendered rigid than the hand. Thus, light strokes from the shoulder downwards have made the arm quite rigid, and the hand only slightly so. These cases, however, are exceptions, and not the rule.

It would be difficult to say whether this is due to a difference of reaction in the various muscles, or simply to the concentration of the subject's attention upon one set of muscles more than the other.

(b) *Inhibition of Movements.*—The next phenomenon characteristic of the second stage is the inability of the subject to carry out movements when told he cannot. One of the easiest movements to prevent is (1) the dropping of an object held in the hand. This is subject to conditions to which I shall return a little later. The other inhibited movements we studied were (2) writing; (3) raising or lowering the arm, and moving the arms laterally when placed straight out in front with the palms together; (4) walking or lifting the leg; (5) rising from a chair or sitting down; (6) picking up an object. The time during which the subject is unable to perform these movements of course varies.

It is easy to prevent the dropping of even a light object held in the hand, if that object be held between the first finger and the thumb. If the thing be held simply by the fingers, without the aid of the thumb, it is extremely difficult to prevent a subject from dropping it, unless it is more or less heavy. A handkerchief, if so held, is dropped by the gradual opening of the hand; a book, which has more weight, cannot, as a rule, be dropped at all. The period of inhibition, as I said, varies in its duration. It lasts longer if the suggestion is continually repeated, and if the subject continues to look at the operator's eyes; and in many cases the forbidden actions cannot be resumed at all unless the suggestion is explicitly removed.

In all these cases of inhibited movements at this early stage, it is not that the subject is unable to contract the muscles necessary to bring about the desired movement, but that he cannot help contracting the antagonistic muscles at the same time. Supposing he is told that he cannot bend his arm, then, when he tries to do so, he contracts the extensors, and the arm remains extended. The degree of contraction of the antagonistic muscles depends partly upon the strength of the suggestion, and partly upon the intensity of the effort with which the subject tries to overcome the inhibition of the suggestion, so that the greater the effort made by the subject, the stronger the contraction of the antagonistic muscles. The suggestion affects the part of the brain which directly or indirectly governs the antagonistic muscles, and every effort to stretch them is at once counteracted.

This seems to be shown by the following experiment: The subject is told he cannot bend his arm, and whilst he is told this someone tries to bend it for him; the extensors immediately contract. Obviously the contraction of the extensors is a reflex from the cortex, brought about by the stimuli set up in attempting to stretch them. The case, no doubt, is the same when he voluntarily contracts his flexors; that is, the effort of will does not act directly on the cortical centre which governs the antagonistic muscles, but only indirectly by stretching these muscles. The same suggestion may act differently in different people. When E. holds a light object in his hand, and is told he cannot drop it, the whole hand grips the object firmly, then slowly relaxes the grip, and so on. J., under similar circumstances, continually passes the object from finger to finger, holding it always between the thumb and one or other of his fingers. Often after the first movement or two all the fingers except one get free, but any movement of this from the object is accompanied by a movement of one of the other fingers to seize it. Thus, the fingers are kept dancing backwards and forwards, towards the thumb,` and the object is still held.

Again, if B. be told that he cannot lift his hand, laid flat on the table, there are movements of his arm, but his hand does not rise ; whilst J., under the same suggestion, lifts one part of the hand after the other from the table until he touches it by the tip of one finger or the thumb ; but as soon as this is raised another finger darts down, and so keeps up a kind of tattoo.

F., when told he could not write his name, tried at first to do so by moving his fingers, but could make nothing but scratches ; it then occurred to him that by using his whole arm he might be able to write. He managed to write the first half of his name in this way, but when he was told that he could not write at all, this movement was rendered ineffective, and resulted only in more scratches.

I here give two more examples of the way in which

a suggestion may work itself out. J. was told that he could not take a step forward. He raised one leg, and put his foot out in front laterally, but could not get it to the ground excepting alongside the other foot. After some trials it struck him that, if he could only lose his balance when one leg was raised with the foot in front, he must come down on it and make the step he was struggling for. So with one leg in the air he made sudden jerks with his body forward, and then presently did lose his balance. But immediately he did so he caught the mantelpiece, which was near him, so breaking the stumble; and he declared that he could not help thus saving himself.

The following example will show how a subject may devise a way of circumventing a suggestion. So many seem to have an idea that a suggestion given in hypnosis is always fulfilled with inexorable fatality, that it is well to bear in mind that this is by no means the case. J.F. was told that he could deal out only twelve cards from a pack—no more. He took the pack and dealt the cards out one by one, counting one, two, three, etc., as he did so. Having dealt the twelve cards, he took the thirteenth card in his hand, but was utterly unable to put it down on the table. After repeating the experiment of dealing cards several times, and being uniformly unsuccessful in dealing out more than twelve, he reflected that if, instead of dealing one card a time, he took two, and still counted one, two, three, as he dealt each pair, he might be able to circumvent the suggestion. He did so readily, dealing out twenty-four cards instead of twelve; but when he took the thirteenth pair and tried to deal that, saying "thirteen," he again found himself unable to put the cards down.

We did not find that the three kinds of phenomena —viz., contracture, inhibition of voluntary movements not included in stage 1, and the execution of movements by imperative suggestion—followed one another in any regular sequence; for, whilst all subjects capable of any of them show those of the first stage, some may show any one of the subdivisions of stage 2 without the others. This happens, however, only with the minority of subjects. Generally speaking, the phenomena can be produced in the following order :

(1) The subject can be prevented from dropping an object.

(2) His arms and hands can be made rigid.

(3) He can be prevented from writing.

(4) He can be made to carry out a movement (stage 3).

Further, as I have said before, all these phenomena are obtained in any subject who shows at all markedly the phenomena of the third stage.

It is to be noticed that, when passes are made before an inhibitory suggestion is given, the inability to make the movement may be due to the contracture produced by the passes, and not to the suggestion itself. In some cases the inhibitory suggestion may be effective when contracture has been produced though it was ineffective before. Thus C., when told that he cannot bend his arm, does so without any hesitation; but if he is first told that his hand and arm are rigid, and then, when they have become rigid, that he cannot bend his arm, the time taken by him to bend it is very considerably prolonged.

In all subjects in whom rigidity is produced there is a marked tendency for a limb to stiffen as soon as attention is fixed on it; thus, if such a subject be asked to hold his arm out, and if he be told that after a little time he will be unable to lower it, it will become rigid even before he tries to move it.

There is one phenomenon—viz., the production of suggested automatic muscular movement—of which I may speak at this point. My attention was first called to it by the Hon. E. Feilding quite lately. I have tried to obtain these movements only with eight subjects. In one case I was unable to produce the effect with a subject whom I could compel to continue movements voluntarily begun. In four I succeeded when I could not compel the subjects to continue such movements. With the others both sets of phenomena could be induced. It appears on the whole to be a phenomenon which lies between the second and third stages, and is, I think, conveniently classed as belonging to the earliest part of the third stage.

So far I have tried the experiment only in one form. The subject, whose eyes are closed by suggestion, lays his right hand on mine. He is then asked to remove his hand voluntarily from mine, and to replace it again every time I count three. I then begin counting, one, two, three, etc., and each time I say "three" he moves his hand an inch or two from mine and then replaces it. After this has been done three or four times, I ask him no longer to move his hand voluntarily, but to let it lie quite passively in mine, trying neither to·move it nor to prevent it from moving. I then tell him that I shall endeavour to make it move automatically, and I begin counting again as before, one, two, three, etc., with rather a long pause at the "three." If the hand does not soon begin to move of itself, a very little pressure, a mere gentle touch, is made each time at the side of his hand or wrist in the direction in which his hand is intended to move, and he is assured that the motion will come in time. After a few trials slight movements begin, and as the experiment goes on they become stronger, until at last, at each "three," the hand is automatically moved completely away from mine and back again.

As a rule, one can then go straight on, telling him to try to keep his hand quite still, since he must move it with or without his will. If the experiment is continued in the same way as before, his hand soon begins to move, notwithstanding his efforts to keep it stationary. Here, of course, is a response to an imperative suggestion, and the phenomenon, therefore, belongs to the third stage ; but there can be no doubt that the previous training in making him move his

6

hand, first voluntarily and then automatically, renders it much more easy to secure this response.

￬*Stage* 3.—The third stage of the waking state is often rather sharply marked from the first two by the possibility of enforcing imperative suggestions. One finds a very large number of subjects who are quite readily amenable to inhibitory suggestions, but on whom no imperative suggestions appear to have any effect whatever.

The inhibitory suggestion merely confirms the state of action or inaction during which it was made; the imperative has to change inaction to action or *vice versa*, and this, perhaps, is the cause of the greater difficulty which one finds in enforcing imperative commands.

To the third stage also belongs the class of suggestions which prevent a subject from stopping a movement voluntarily begun; and later in this stage loss of memory for particular facts can sometimes be induced, so that a subject may be made to forget his own name.

To compel a subject to execute a movement, the command must be repeated over and over again, often for a minute or two in difficult cases, before any perceptible effect is produced. It certainly often helps matters considerably if the subject continues to look at the operator's eyes while the suggestions are made. This, however, is not a necessary concomitant, as success can often be obtained while the eyes are closed. In imperative as in inhibitory suggestions, every grade of intensity of effect exists. In subjects who are only in the second stage no effect whatever is produced. In a slightly deeper condition the subject feels an inclination to perform the suggested act, but can resist without any appreciable effort. As the condition deepens, the effort required to resist the suggestion becomes greater and greater. Thus, if a subject be told to get up from his chair, he will, after a short time, actually hold his chair with both hands in order to prevent himself from getting up. Others cannot successfully resist at all, however great the effort they make, and some are quite incapable of even attempting to resist in the slightest degree.

As the suggestion is repeated, and the idea gains in strength, the aspect of the subject usually changes completely. At first he may wear an expression of amused indifference; but gradually his countenance becomes more serious, as he begins to feel that, after all, it is not easy to resist, and at last his whole attitude becomes of striking, almost strenuously fixed, attention.

The following were the principal movements which were tried during the experiments at Cambridge. The subject was made :

(1) To laugh ;
(2) To walk to the operator ;
(3) To rise from his chair ;
(4) To flex his arm ;
(5) To close his eyes ;
(6) To open his eyes.

At first in these cases all the muscles are quiescent, then the muscles antagonistic to the movement come into play, and finally the muscles required to bring it about.

The readiness with which a subject can be compelled to laugh varies very much in different cases, according to temperament. Some people never or scarcely ever laugh, and in these, naturally, laughter cannot be excited during hypnosis. In making the suggestion of laughter the operator may remain as grave as he pleases. When he succeeds, it is sometimes impossible for the subject to stop laughing until told to do so. In some the laughter ceases spontaneously soon after the suggestion is given, unless, of course, it is renewed.

Habits of life tell on other suggestions besides that of laughter. Thus, I have often suggested to a subject that he shall strike a false chord while playing the piano. This may succeed with anyone, but I have found it impossible in the case of two really musical subjects, though always easy 'in the case of those who could merely strum.

In the third stage we can also prevent a subject from stopping a movement voluntarily begun; this can often be done before he can be made to initiate a movement. The most usual movements thus continued were laughing, moving thumbs or hands round one another, repeating words or phrases, beating time with the hands or feet.

The subject is asked to make some continuous

movement, and, after half a minute or so, is told that he cannot stop. It is a remarkable fact that the suggestion "You must go on" is often quite ineffective when the suggestion "You cannot stop" acts quite readily. I have noted this very frequently, and I always consider that a subject who responds to "You must" is in a distinctly deeper condition than the one who merely responds to "You cannot."

I have never once failed with the negative form of the suggestion when the imperative has succeeded, though I have frequently failed with "You must" after success with "You cannot." It seems to be a law almost without exception that the inhibitory is more powerful than the imperative form of suggestion. Only fairly susceptible subjects pass into this stage without prolonged hypnotic processes.

Suggested loss of memory for particular facts is a phenomenon which is liable to a good deal of variation. In general it appeals easier to induce than the phenomena of stage 4, but often it could be realized only in a later state of hypnosis.

The subject may try hard to remember, and fail; and not infrequently he may present the curious condition of being unable to try to remember at all.

⤶*Stage 4.*—In this we can produce:

    (1) Loss of sensation in the skin.

    (2) Imperfect delusions.

These latter are most easily evoked in relation to touch and temperature; thus, a light body may seem heavy, or a cold body hot, and the subject may be made to feel hot or cold. A paper-knife may become heavy enough to weigh the hand of the subject to the ground. Again, it may seem too hot to hold, and it is odd to see a subject fling it down, instantly regarding his hand, as though expecting to find the mark of burning. In the fifth stage we also get visual illusions, memory afterwards being sometimes imperfect.

So far there is no marked change in the appearance of the subject: the face shows neither drowsiness nor heaviness, and the only noticeable change is a certain intentness of attention towards the operator, and possibly dilatation of the pupils. Still, until a suggestion has been made, it is impossible to say whether it will be successful or not. When the hypnotic processes are further prolonged, the appearance of the subject will often give an indication, though not an infallible one, of the suggestions that will be effective; thus there is:

(1) More or less drowsiness, which is accompanied by an almost complete absence of initiative, the subject remaining quiescent except when he means to obey a suggestion.

(2) A disinclination to make any voluntary effort.

(3) Disposition towards catalepsy.

It is not easy to divide the later states of hypnotism into stages. In all the different deeper states, except, perhaps, that of somnambulism (our final stage), some illusions can be induced easily, others only with difficulty; and we found, as, indeed, has been almost universally noticed, that in different subjects there is great variation on awaking in the degree of memory of what had happened in the hypnotized state. In both of these matters, really, there is every possible variation.

After hypnotic passes have been continued for a varying time, illusions can be induced, and the subject may act in accordance with them. Sometimes one could tell from the appearance of the subject whether the attempt would be successful or not. We generally tried first to make the subject hear illusory bells, then to see an illusory light, and then to make a speech to an illusory audience. When these illusions were successful, all the phenomena of the previous states could be readily obtained. The subject was cataleptic, and kept his arms raised if they had been put in that position. If told to open his eyes, he still could not put his arms down. They remained fixed, the muscles being apparently in a state of contracture; if an object was swept over his eyes, they closed; if a light was brought near, the pupils contracted. When a suggestion requiring action is given, the catalepsy ceases at once, and the appearance of the subject becomes very nearly, if not quite, indistinguishable from normal. When the illusion is ended—and in some cases this can be done by simply closing the eyes—the cataleptic state returns. If the illusion be concluded by closing the eyes, the limbs often remain in the position of the moment. If it is ended by verbal suggestion, the muscles return to

their normal state. Taste can be dulled, but not
abolished. The readiest class of illusions, after those
mentioned above, are those connected with the touch
—for instance, contact with flies, or fleas, or a snake—
or with the sight of objects which lead to action or
strong emotion, such as a snake on the ground.

When an illusive object is shown on a piece of
paper, the subject sees it more quickly if the real
object is first shown him. For instance, if he is told
there is a drawing of a rabbit on a blank piece of
paper, he will see it more readily if a drawing of a
rabbit is first shown him and a copy of it is asserted
to be on the blank paper. As an instance of the
difference in the ease with which illusions can be
induced, I may mention M. Being hypnotized, he
was shown a blank card, and told that there was a
drawing of a fly upon it; but, though the suggestion
was repeated several times, he still replied that he
did not see it. Then it was suggested : "The fly has
escaped; it is buzzing about you; there are many
flies round your head," when he began to brush them
off his face, and strike at them in the air with great
energy. So also a subject will more readily see an
illusory picture of someone familiar than that of an
unfamiliar object. His memory of the actions he has
performed during the day seems more or less dulled,
but reflection or slight suggestion soon recalls them.
After any suggestion has taken effect, and he is asked
what he is thinking of, he answers "Nothing." His
state varies somewhat, so that at one time the same

suggestion may require more repetition and insistence to be effective than at another. Possibly this is due to some suggestions or acts partially waking him, or to a long pause between two suggestions, when he becomes a trifle more deeply hypnotized. If an action, such as swinging the arms, be begun for the subject, he will continue it himself.

All our subjects in this stage, on whom Langley and I experimented together, would take suggestions from either of us; often, however, subjects will take no suggestion in the deep state except from the hypnotizer, and I found this frequently to be the case in those subjects on whom I was experimenting myself when others tried to make suggestions. On awaking, the subject would remember more or less accurately all that had taken place.

The above stage is a distinct state of hypnosis in certain subjects. They can easily be sent into it, and they remain in it almost indefinitely.

L. passed into this state in from ten to twenty seconds. In his case the most effective means for its production was to close his eyes and press gently upon them. The readiness with which he accepted suggestions was increased by lightly stroking the top of his head. Thus, after making one or two experiments, he was shown a blank card, and told that it was a photograph of a friend in the room. Asked if he recognized it, he said " No "; and when again told that it was a photograph and that he must see it, he still answered " No." His eyes were closed, half a dozen strokes were made backwards over the top of his head, and he was then told to open his eyes. He was then shown a card with a circle on it, and told, "Look at this photograph of F.; it is an excellent photograph." This was repeated several times, during which he looked in a rather puzzled way at the card. "Don't you think it good?" "No." "What is the matter with it?" "It is misty." "But it is something like him?" "Yes, it is something like him." When awakened, and asked what he remembered, he said he had been shown a card with a circle on it, and told it was a photograph of F., but that he did not see any photograph. Here, then, the subject, although not seeing the object suggested, behaves and talks as if he did; and when asked why, says that he could not help himself. That he had not merely forgotten having seen it is shown by his ability to recall the conversation about it, and also by the fact that when passes were made for some time longer, and the experiment was tried again, he remembered when awake having been shown a blank card, and then later a photograph on it.

Stage 5.—When passes are continued longer, the senses become more dulled, and illusions are still more readily produced. Anæsthesia can be produced by suggestion.

The memory is very imperfect on awakening, and often is entirely gone. Even when our subjects did recollect some of the events during hypnosis, they would always underrate the time the experiment had taken, and would say, perhaps, ten minutes or a quarter of an hour, instead of one hour or one and a half hours.

If a visual hallucination be induced, and afterwards changed to another, and this again to another, and so on, it will generally be found that the subject, when aroused, remembers the first hallucination more or less perfectly, but that memory of the succeeding hallucinations is uncertain or even completely absent.

One illusion which I generally produced was that of seeing a bright star or light in the ceiling. The subject would stand in front of me, and look at my eyes for about a minute, while I made light strokes over his brows and temples. Then I would look up, point upwards, and say : "Look at that star ; isn't it bright? Look, it is getting brighter ; watch it." The subject usually stares upwards with a fixed gaze, and remains immobile for an indefinite time; and if asked whether the star is bright, and whether he sees it, answers "Yes." After a time the suggestion is made that it is getting darker, and that the star is fading away, and at last that it is gone. Almost any other hallucination can then be readily induced. Thus, he can be made to believe that he sees a snake, that he is in a boat, that he is on horseback, etc. ; but, when aroused, though he will as a rule remember the first hallucination of the star perfectly, those succeeding will be confusedly recollected or entirely forgotten.

In both the fourth and fifth stages mimicry of

actions occurs—more perfectly in the latter than in the former. In the fourth stage the attention of the subject must be directed to the act in order to produce mimicry. It seems most probable that mimicry is due to suggestion. We take it to be a reflex from the cortex of the brain: the act performed before the subject gives rise to the idea (unconscious) of the movement, which leads to the imitation of the said movement.

Heidenhain attributes mimicry to reflex actions not involving the cortex, apparently because in his subjects auditory suggestions were ineffective.

Stage 6 is marked by somnambulism, suggested anæsthesia, anosmia, etc. The subject attends to the hypnotizer only, is suggestible only by him, and has no memory on awaking.

Effect of Telling to Sleep.—This varies greatly. In some subjects it produces the outward sign of going to sleep, but does not—in a short time, at any rate—otherwise alter the hypnotic state. In others it has an astounding effect, producing almost instantly deep hypnotic sleep, with complete loss of memory on awaking.

It has generally been considered that hyperæsthesia of one or more of the senses is among the earliest signs of somnambulism. Braid, Bernheim, and Gurney so record it. As far as our experiments went, however, it did not appear that the hypnotic processes of gazing, passes, and suggestion of sleep ever produced hyperæsthesia, but that this stage required special excitation for its production. It is readily produced in stage 5, and can be brought about by direct suggestion or by continued conversation.

Summary of the Stages as found in our Experiments.

Stage 1.—Those voluntary movements can be inhibited by direct suggestion which are most commonly carried out by reflex action in ordinary life.

Stage 2.—Contracturè can be produced. Voluntary movements not included in stage 1 can be inhibited.

Stage 3.—The subject can be prevented from stopping a movement voluntarily begun, and made to initiate a movement. Loss of memory for particular facts can be suggested.

Stage 4.—Loss of cutaneous sensation can be produced. Imperfect delusions can be suggested. Memory afterwards nearly or quite perfect.

Stage 5.—Senses more dulled. Visual and other illusions can be induced. Memory afterwards imperfect.

Stage 6.—Somnambulism. Anæsthesia, anosmia, etc., can be suggested. The subject attends to hypnotizer only. No memory on awaking.

Such are the stages when hypnosis is induced by the method described above, without any suggestion of sleep being made at the commencement.

Comparison with Stages of Liébeault and Bernheim.

I have mentioned before that Liébeault and Bernheim have classified the stages of hypnosis according to the maximum degree of hypnotization to be obtained in different individuals in successive trials. It will be convenient to consider at once how far their stages agree with those that are given above.

First degree of Liébeault and Bernheim : The subjects feel more or less torpor, heaviness of the eyes, and drowsiness. A variety of the first degree they consider to be the state in which the subject " n'ont pas de somnolence à proprement parler," but in which he is unable to open his eyes when told that he cannot. This variety we took to be a typical characteristic, for if the hypnotic processes are prolonged, there is no one who would not probably feel some heaviness and drowsiness.

In the second degree of Liébeault and Bernheim (light sleep) the subject is more or less cataleptic. So long as nothing is done the muscles remain flaccid, but when a limb is gently moved it stays in the position in which it has been placed. The catalepsy has various degrees. The limb raised may, after a second or two, sink down. If the whole arm be raised it falls, but if the forearm be raised it is kept up ; or while the forearm is kept raised the fingers may not retain the position in which they are placed, or the limb may be kept raised only if it is held there for a second or two. The intermediate stages between the first and second degree occur when the subject keeps the cataleptic position, unless he is told that he cannot help it, when he moves the limb, and when a subject does not leave his limbs in any position unless it is defined to him by suggestion. It seems likely that there are three constantly consecutive states here confused. In the first the subject is more or less cataleptic when a limb is raised and gently stroked once or twice; but, though told he cannot move it, he can always do so. In the second he is cataleptic, as before; but if told that he cannot move a limb which is in catalepsy, he cannot do it for a time in consequence of the simultaneous contracture of the muscles antagonistic to the action. In the third he is cataleptic, as before; but if told that he cannot move a limb which is in catalepsy, he is unable to do so, although the antagonistic muscles do not contract. This is quite a different state from the second—it is paresis, or paralysis of the muscles. The development of these stages does not follow very closely the development of the stages without drowsiness. The catalepsy between their first and second degree appears to correspond to the inability to make movements in consequence of contraction of the antagonistic muscles in division 2 of our second stage, but is much less developed than when the subject is not drowsy. Paresis and paralysis occur between stages 2 and 3. In this condition there may be slight loss of memory, but only such as may be seen in an inattentive person.

In Liébeault and Bernheim's third degree (deep sleep) the subject is unable to stop a movement which he has begun when told he cannot do so. This is division 1 of our third stage, but in their fourth degree tactile sensibility may be dulled or abolished. This we never observed except as the result of direct suggestion. Lastly, they can obtain "contracture suggestive." This is division 1 of our stage 2. We have always been able to obtain this before we could prevent a subject from stopping a movement already begun.

Their fourth stage (their very deep state) is characterized by the subjects hearing the operator alone, unless he puts them into relation with other persons. Excepting when the subject was in a state of somnambulism, either of us had no difficulty in producing all the illusions which could be produced by the other. Possibly this was because our subjects regarded both of us in the light of hypnotizers. When experimenting apart from Langley, I often found that the subject would not obey suggestions from strangers, but only from myself. But Langley and I could produce this condition in our fifth stage. If either of us told the subject that he could hear no one but himself, the other would then speak in vain.

The fifth degree of Liébeault and Bernheim (light somnambulism) corresponds with our fifth stage as given before, except that we found the subjects sometimes obeyed others as well as the hypnotizer, and that sensation was not abolished except by suggestion.

Their sixth degree is one in which the subject himself has no recollection of what he has done while hypnotized.

CHAPTER V

OTHER HYPNOTIC PHENOMENA

Hallucinations—Post-hypnotic suggestion—Negative hallucinations—Anæsthesia—Other phenomena (Effects of passes—Effects of previous deep hypnotization on experimental subjects—Self-suggestion—Effects on sense of touch and temperature—Light sensory stimuli and suggestion).

I. Hallucinations.

As the previous chapter indicated, it is often possible to induce the condition of somnambulism without any direct suggestion of sleep, merely by evoking hallucinations. It frequently happens, therefore, that a subject in stage 5 will spontaneously pass into stage 6, if illusions are induced. Some subjects may lapse suddenly into somnambulism while they are in quite an early stage, but this rarely occurs unless they have been hypnotized on former occasions, and experienced somnambulism then. In other cases the suggestion of sleep induces somnambulism, and this is the method most commonly employed. But it must be remembered that the proportion of subjects susceptible of somnambulism is not great—something under 20 per cent.

Numberless experiments have been made with hallucinations. It is certain that some subjects, when they act as though hallucinated, are not really so, but are compelled to act as though they were, as in the case of L., mentioned above. But I have often had subjects who remembered their illusions, and to whom the hallucinations appeared real experiences; and probably in somnambulism this is the rule.

One of the most interesting studies in connection with visual hallucinations is the behaviour of the subject as regards a suggested illusory picture on a blank sheet of paper. We made a number of experiments in this at Cambridge. The subject was made to see some illusion of a small picture, say of a pink shell, on a perfectly circular disc of white cardboard, and asked to copy it. He would begin to make a drawing, glancing every few seconds at the illusory picture which he was supposed to be copying. If his attention was distracted for a moment, and the circular disc turned out of its original position without his being aware of it, he at once recognized the fact when he resumed the drawing of his copy, and would rearrange it as it was at first. When he looked at the imaginary shell through Iceland spar it appeared doubled, and if the Iceland spar was slowly revolved while he looked through it, the two images appeared to revolve round each other, just as if the original image were actual. It was quite clear from the experiments that subjects notice extremely small marks, and attach them to the hallucinatory images.

In many cases they recognize a blank card, which, they have been told, is a picture of some kind, and pick it out quite easily when it is mixed with a number of apparently exactly similar ones.

L., mentioned above, could do this, and could also remember that he recognized the card by minute marks, but in his normal state he was totally unable to distinguish it.

II. Post-Hypnotic Suggestions.

But the most striking phenomenon of somnambulism is that of post-hypnotic suggestion. Post-hypnotic suggestions may succeed in the deep state, and even earlier, before somnambulism is reached, but those given during somnambulism work out most strikingly and perfectly. Suggestions given in this way act more powerfully than others, owing, perhaps, in a measure to the fact that the patient carries them out without knowing consciously that they are due to suggestion, so that deliberate resistance is absent.

It is still a matter of dispute whether the subject is in a normal condition during the performance in his waking state of an action which has been suggested during his sleep. Some subjects certainly are in an abnormal state, for, having carried out the suggested act, they forget all about it, and are quite unaware that it has been accomplished. For the moment they appear to have returned to the state of somnambulism. But a large number remember their action perfectly well, and their condition is not distinguishable from the normal. If, however, hallucinations are thus induced, I have observed that during their persistence the subject often presents an appearance of abstraction which is not natural to his normal state.

The experimental enforcement of a post-hypnotic suggestion, as a rule, presents but little difficulty. The patient may be told that he will perform the action either on awakening, or at some particular hour, or after some specified event. I have often told a subject that he will do some trivial action, such as ight or blow out a candle, when I look at my watch. A very considerable length of time may be made to elapse between the making of a suggestion and its accomplishment. Some twenty years ago I suggested to a subject who was deeply hypnotized that exactly a year after he should see me come into his room while he was at breakfast, that I should say "Good-morning," and then vanish ; and this succeeded after even that lapse of time. The person concerned, how-ever, was extraordinarily suggestible—the best subject, I think, that I have ever seen.

But though it is generally easy to enforce these suggestions, it is not always so, even in subjects who carry out other than post-hypnotic suggestions readily. Occasionally one meets subjects who will not respond to even the simplest post-hypnotic suggestion, but such resistance is not common. And in many of these cases I have found that, if the subject be instructed to do something on awakening, he will generally obey if he be made during his sleep to state what he has to do, so as to ensure that he really understands. For he is sometimes so lethargic that he cannot assimilate a suggestion unless he is partly roused; making him repeat the suggestion, and so ascertaining that he has comprehended it, overcomes this difficulty.

The subject of negative hallucinations and anæsthesia properly belongs to the deep state and somnambulism, though anæsthesia can sometimes be induced in the earlier stages.

III. Increased Powers of Memory.

In the deep stage the range of memory may extend farther back, often very much farther than it does in the normal condition, and a subject may be able to recall events of his earliest childhood. This extension of memory is not limited to the deep state, though it is then more marked. Even in the earlier stages a subject may be able to recall memories of a long forgotten past. In one case, mentioned in the next chapter, I made a lady aged thirty-two remember herself in long clothes, and some of the incidents which she recalled were afterwards verified.

This increased power of memory is of great importance from a therapeutical standpoint. Instances of its use will be found in the next chapter.

IV. Negative Hallucinations.

A negative hallucination is that in which the sensation of a real nerve stimulus is unperceived. I have often suggested to somnambulic subjects that I, or some other person in the room, am invisible. They then cease to notice the invisible person, and may even sit down on his lap instead of the chair, which they imagine to be empty. But it is clear from their behaviour that they generally do realize the supposedly invisible person or thing, though perhaps not in the same vivid manner as that in which they see other people, seeming to be aware of the cancelled presence in a dreamy kind of way, as if only a part, and not the whole, of the consciousness perceived it. That such a subject actually may realize the invisible person is shown by the following experiment, which I often made with some of my Cambridge subjects. I could hypnotize many whom I had hypnotized on previous occasions by suddenly gazing intensely at them. They would often pass instantly into deep sleep, with catalepsy. I have frequently made myself invisible to those subjects, but even when one of them acted as though he could not see me, I found that if I caught his eye, and suddenly gazed intently at him, he always immediately passed into catalepsy, thus showing conclusively that he had really perceived me.

The subject may be made colour-blind to different colours, and experiments on the complementary colours of invisible, as well as of suggested hallucinatory, colours were made on our Cambridge subjects, but these are beyond the province of this book. It is possible to induce negative hallucinations of the other senses as well. Thus the subject may be rendered incapable of hearing a particular person speak, or of tasting sweet or bitter, though the sense of taste is more difficult to influence.

V. Anæsthesia.

But the most interesting of all the negative hallucinations is certainly the cutaneous anæsthesia and analgesia which can be evoked by suggestion. Suggested anæsthesia, as seen during hypnosis, is simply the non-perception of the particular sensation which the subject has been told that he cannot feel, the other cutaneous sensations remaining intact. It is easier to abolish or diminish sensations of touch than the sensations of heat and cold, and the abolition of the sense of touch is generally accompanied by rigidity of the limb experimented on.

But the condition is one of great complexity. Take the following simple experiment, which I tried on several people. Having concealed the subject's hand from his view by means of a simply-arranged screen, I suggested that he would be unable to feel a prick with one point of a pair of compasses, but that he would feel at once if pricked with both points. I found that I could draw blood without making him flinch if I pricked him with one point; but he rebelled immediately if I pricked him with both points. Also, he could be made to feel the touch of soft cotton-wool, and yet be quite impervious to a sharp needle prick, and in one case even to the scorch of a burning match,

Here the subject clearly must in some way perceive both sensations; but, in addition, he must mentally differentiate between the two, and reject one, while he accepts the other, and allows himself to feel it. It is very difficult to form any lucid idea of this complex act, but I believe that the result is due, not merely to a failure to perceive, but also to an inhibition of his power to conceive the forbidden sensation. This theory may explain the following experiment, which I made on one or two subjects at Cambridge, and on one since I left there.

The subject, whom I had hypnotized on previous occasions, and who, I knew, could be readily rendered anæsthetic, was asked to sit in an arm-chair. I then placed his hands on the arms of the chair, but in doing so passed his palm lightly over the bristles of a brush which I had fixed to the outside of one of the arms, so that he could not see it. I then immediately suggested that the hand could feel nothing. When next I asked him what I had done to his hand before rendering it anæsthetic, he could not recall anything. When sensation was restored, however, he immediately remembered that his hand had been passed over a brush or some similar surface. By rendering him anæsthetic immediately after the stimulus had been applied, I gave no time for the sensations to be linked up with other ideas by association. Probably he could not recall the stimulus, because the power of conceiving such a sensation 'was temporarily inhibited, but I have not made the experiment often enough to be sure that suggestion was entirely eliminated.

The rest of this chapter is devoted to the effects of light stimuli and to the brief consideration of certain other phenomena which have not been mentioned in the previous chapter. The experiments described were made by Professor Langley and myself on Cambridge undergraduates.

VI. Other Phenomena.

1. *Certain Effects of Passes.*—During the waking state, contracture, as mentioned before, can often be produced by passes, each downward stroke causing a little further contraction, and each upward stroke or pass a decrease of contraction.

O., for instance, when his fingers are stroked downwards, gets his hand more and more extended until the fingers become rigid. Stroking in the opposite direction over any one finger causes slight relaxation in it. Thus, according to the number of up-and-down strokes, different fingers can be brought into any degree of stiffness.

This general effect of reverse passes and strokes is well known. The following experiments will show certain further details; they were first tried on a waking subject, A. After a variable number of strokes the fingers, or any one of them, became insensitive to needle-pricks, or to induction currents of moderate strength, and to the strokes of the operating finger itself. A. sat down and passed his hand through a hole in a screen, resting it, palm downwards, on a table on the other side. Thus he was unable to see his hand or us, and could not tell what we were doing to it. He was asked to say " Yes " when he felt anything touch his hand. When a stroke was made downwards, he said nothing; when a stroke was made upwards, he said "Yes." This was perfectly constant, so that with up and down strokes he felt those made upwards but not those made downwards. If the upwards were repeated several times in succession, the next following down stroke would be felt, but the subsequent ones were not.

This state of insensibility is associated with sensory stimuli, starting in the upper part of the finger and progressing downwards. The restoration to the normal state has thus become associated with sensory stimuli progressing in the opposite direction. The ordinary effect of reverse passes is to restore the part to its normal condition. In the stage of moderate insensibility, which I have mentioned above, each upward stroke produces a temporary return to the normal, but is insufficient to destroy the effect of the more numerous downward strokes.

This phenomenon can also be produced in the fourth and fifth stages of hypnotism. This we verified in two subjects, B. and S. In S. the second and third fingers were after some time rendered rigid and insensitive by downward strokes. S. was told to say "Yes," when he felt anything touch his hand. When the first and fourth fingers or thumb were touched, he said "Yes." When the second and third fingers were touched, he said nothing. The second finger was then stroked upwards half a dozen times without producing any effect. It was bent and unbent, and stroked upwards for about half a minute, until at last he said "Yes." Then the slightest movement upwards was felt, but stroking downwards was not. It was sufficient even lightly to drag a needle, laid flat, on the finger upwards, without moving it over the surface of the skin.

2. *Persistence in the Earlier Stages of Changes induced in Deep Stages.*—As has already been said, when a subject has once been deeply hypnotized great care must be taken in drawing any deductions from his subsequent behaviour in the light stages of hypnotism. This is necessary, because some of the phenomena formerly induced in the deep stages can afterwards be obtained in the light stages. Apparently Bernheim's observations on the waking phenomena were made only on subjects who had previously been deeply hypnotized. Although possibly this persistence of impression may be related to the phenomena of post-hypnotic suggestion, it must not be confused with it. A good example is shown by the possibility of producing anæsthesia in the waking stage if this has once been produced in the deeper state. Thus, in S. neither passes, stroking, nor suggestion produced contracture or anæsthesia in the waking state; in B. we could produce contracture, but not anæsthesia, in the waking state; but, after they had been deeply

hypnotized, and anæsthesia induced in the deep state
by suggestion, we could subsequently induce anæsthesia
in the waking state. The effects of suggestion frequently persist long after the suggestion has been
removed. Thus, M.'s strength was tested with a
dynamometer. Paralysis of the arm was then suggested. He did not recover his strength for some
time after he had been told that his arm was restored
to its normal state ; and the result was the same when
the trial was made during deep hypnosis, or immediately after waking.

3. *Self-Suggestion.*—Many subjects can to a certain
extent bring themselves into the states induced by the
hypnotizer. Practice increases this power. L. could
readily send himself into a condition in which delusions
could occur ; D., by stroking his eyes and thinking of
being unable to open them, soon found himself unable
to do so ; he could do the same with one eye, leaving
the other in its normal state. The power of the
subject to induce contracture in himself has various
stages. For instance, in making the hand rigid these
are :

(*a*) The subject thinks of contracture and makes
passes over his hand.

(*b*) He looks at his hand and thinks of contracture.

(*c*) He thinks of contracture without looking at his
hand.

Thus, B. was able to do (*a*), but not (*c*). When his
hand was put through a screen, he was unable to

stiffen it himself. C. developed great power in this direction, and, when laid across three chairs, with his head on the first and his heels on the last, he could gradually make his whole body rigid, so that the middle chair could be taken away, while he still kept his position without any strain, a position which he was entirely unable to maintain unless he caused his muscles thus to pass into contracture. Still, even in this case contracture came on more readily if someone made passes over his body. He was also able, to a considerable degree, to prevent contracture coming on when passes or strokes were made over his hand or arm—so much so that, though the hand or arm became stiff, he had not more than a momentary hesitation in moving them when he tried.

F. and H. put their hands in front of them, palm to palm, and then, thinking of being unable to part them, found that they were for a time unable to do so. In these cases the arms became rigid, and the force required to part them seemed to be greater than that required when the subject exerted his maximum voluntary effort to prevent his arms from being separated. F. at first could prevent himself from separating his hands only by closing his eyes and imagining the operator looking at him; later he could do it without this. Apparently all the above phenomena are due to contracture. J. states that it is possible, by imagining himself unable to remember some simple thing, to prevent himself for a time from remembering it. It is noteworthy that the power of self-suggestion has no direct relation to the degree of susceptibility to hypnotism; in fact, the occurrence of self-suggestion in a previously good hypnotic subject did in some cases decrease his susceptibility to hypnotic suggestion to a very considerable extent. On the other hand, a large number of good hypnotic subjects appeared to be unable to produce the slightest effect upon themselves by self-suggestion.

4. *Effects on the Senses of Touch and Temperature.*—Heidenhain has mentioned that in the one-sided catalepsy which may result from striking the top of the head, the sense of touch disappears from the cataleptic arm before the sense of temperature. We also found this to be the case when strokes or passes were made over an area of the skin in subjects susceptible of a certain degree of anæsthesia. We generally experimented as follows :

The subject, without any hypnotic process having been performed on him, was asked to put both his hands through a screen on a table, and to say when he felt anything touching or near his hands, and also to say what he felt—whether warmth or chill, a touch or a prick, and so on. Passes or strokes over one of the fingers were next made; then at short intervals this finger and the other parts of his hand as well were touched with a needle, or a weight was placed on them, the temperature of which was noted. In this way we found that, while the subject felt normally in all parts of his hand except the finger operated upon, in this the sensation of touch, and of moderately severe pricks with the needle, disappeared at a time when he could still recognize at once warm or cold objects. Thus a 20-gramme brass weight at the temperature of his hand was not felt when laid on the finger operated upon, while similar weights, either hotter or colder, were readily felt. Thus, too, if the finger operated upon and that next to it were simultaneously stroked, he would say : " You are passing something warm over one finger and stroking the other." Strokes or passes made the anæsthesia more definite, so that only very strong induction shocks were felt, while at the same time the sense of temperature was dulled, so that the hot or cold body was not felt at once, as it was elsewhere, but only after an interval of two or three seconds. It is difficult to make out clearly exactly at what point the sense of warmth disappears, since the application of a warm body tends to do away with the anæsthesia. Thus, after the application of a hot weight to an insensitive area of skin for a very short period, it becomes sensitive to the prick of a needle. This does not occur after the application of a cold weight; but our experiments were too few to prove more than the main fact of the disappearance of the tactile sense, and the slight loss of the sense of pain before there is any appreciable diminution of the sense of temperature.

5. *Light Sensory Stimuli and Suggestion.*—It is not easy to separate the effects of suggestion from those of light sensory stimuli. Braid and most subsequent observers have attributed an effect to both. Bernheim

considers that, though passes and such light sensory stimuli may have results, they owe this effect mainly to aiding suggestion, much as an energetic gesture or an impressive demeanour increases the same power. The difficulty here concerns the meaning of the word "suggestion." Its first and obvious meaning implies that the subject is conscious of the prompting, and that he has a conscious idea of the result which the hypnotizer attempts to obtain. It is to this sense that the term "suggestion" should be limited; but the meaning may be extended to include the formation of an unconscious idea—*i.e.*, the production of those changes in the brain which occur in the formation of an idea without those changes which cause the idea to become conscious. Since, however, probably no sensory stimuli can affect the cortex of the brain without giving rise to those changes which are fundamental to the formation of an idea, the extended term "suggestion" would seem merely a way of saying that the light sensory stimuli which cause hypnotic phenomena do so by acting on the cerebral cortex. This, at any rate, appears to be the case in all the phenomena we observed; but, as we made few experiments on the deepest stages, it may be possible that in these stages some of the phenomena may be due to reflex actions from the lower centres of the brain or from the spinal cord, without any change in the cortex. At any rate, there appears to be no doubt that (a) sensory stimuli may give rise to a hypnotic phenomenon without the subject's having a conscious idea of the phenomenon before it occurs; (b) that sensory stimuli of which the subject is not conscious may produce hypnotic phenomena.

Many effects produced by sensory stimuli in the deeper hypnotic stages appeared to show this; but, as in these stages it was impossible to prove whether the subject was unconscious or not, the conclusions are based on the observations made in the early stages, in which the subject could say whether he did or did not feel. It may be suggested that we were completely at the mercy of the subject, and that, except when we applied strong induction currents, he could deceive us as he liked. If (b) can be shown, it may appear to be necessary to show (a) as well, as the two states differ in that in (a) the subject is conscious that something is being done, whilst in (b) he is unconscious of it; it may, therefore, be worth while to deal with them separately. With regard to (a), when the hand of the subject is stroked, producing first rigidity, then loss of sensation, even supposing that it was suspected that loss of sensation might follow rigidity (and some subjects averred they had no expectation of that), it is, we think, certain that none of them had any idea that the sense of touch would disappear before the sense of temperature. When one or more fingers of the hand passed through a screen are made insensitive, they recover sensation, if left alone, in a minute or two; but if continuously stroked, and very lightly, so as to avoid a pull on the rest of the hand, the fingers remain insensitive. With regard to (*b*), the difficulty with many of our subjects was that, when a pass was made over any part of the hand, the whole hand and also the whole arm became rigid. Besides this, when a hand was extended behind a screen, after a few experiments it would often become rigid, even when nothing was done to it. The simple expectation that something was to be done was quite sufficient to cause contracture. In such cases, when the hand became rigid after passes, and the subject declared that he had not felt anything near that hand, the stiffness might have been caused by self-suggestion, and not by unfelt passes, so that no reliable conclusion could be drawn, except after a long series of experiments, comparing the number of times when spontaneous rigidity occurred with the number of times stiffness occurred after unfelt passes or other similar light stimuli.

Such a method at the best is imperfect. Cases, therefore, in which spontaneous rigidity occurred are here omitted, except the following example, in which there was a movement simultaneously with each unfelt movement of the operator's hand. H. placed his hand through a screen, and passes were made three or four inches above it. The hand gradually closed, a slight closing movement occurring at each pass. Eighteen passes were made before the hand was completely shut. During twelve, which were made at irregular intervals, the hand shut only when a pass was made, but after these a movement sometimes took place between the passes. H. declared that he felt nothing, except that his hand was closing. Of course, it is possible that the passes coincided in time with the spontaneous movements of the hands, but this chance is extremely, unlikely. The most satisfactory cases are those in which the hands do not become spontaneously rigid, and in which the fingers can be made rigid and insensitive separately. Gurney recorded a case which very nearly fulfilled these conditions, and he found, when the fingers of the operator were held above one of the fingers of the subject, that nearly always that finger, and that alone, became insensitive. We did not meet with any case so satisfactory as his. With A., however, there was considerable, but not complete, insensibility, which was for a time, at any rate, confined to the part operated upon ; and during an experiment of an hour's duration spontaneous rigidity or insensibility did not occur once.

The following experiment was the first to be made on A., and is given here, since he was then least likely to know our object : He extended both hands through the screen, placing them palm downwards on a table, with the fingers separated. We made passes at about an inch distance over the first and second fingers of his left hand. After about a dozen passes the fingers and various parts of the hand were lightly pricked with a needle, and he was asked to say "Yes" when he felt it. He said "Yes" except when the last two joints of the first and second fingers of the left hand were pricked. These were then pricked hard without his taking any notice. A few passes were next made over the same two fingers, and a 20-gramme brass weight at the temperature of the room, producing a distinctly cold feeling when touching the skin, was placed on one or other of the fingers. As soon as it touched any part of the hand, except the two end joints of the first and second fingers, he said "Yes." When it was placed• on these he said " Yes, something cold," in time varying from three to ten seconds according to the different joints. We asked him: " Do you know whether any passes have been made?" "No." " Are any of your fingers stiff?"   A. then began to lift his hand from the table as a preliminary to closing them. Langley said : " Stop! Cannot you tell without moving your hands?"   "No; both hands are cold."   " Well, try to shut them."   The right hand closed at once, the left slowly, the first and second fingers remaining stretched out after the others.

In such cases there can be little doubt that a state of expectation that some part of the hand will be sent into contracture and made insensitive greatly aids, if, indeed, it is not necessary to, the effect of unfelt passes. The following case shows that the state of expectation is sometimes essential to success : C3, whom I had previously hypnotized, and whose hands could readily be made insensitive, was asked to put his hands through a screen, as above. I tried, by passes and by pointing at his fingers, to render them insensitive, without making any suggestion as to what I was going to do, but failed entirely. I then said : " I am going to try to take away sensation from the different parts of your hand without your knowledge." After this I succeeded perfectly.

As the hand passes from contracture to insensitiveness in the early states, the following changes usually take place: First, the hand is in contracture ; there is no change in temperature and no loss of sensation. A little later, however, the hand is contracted without, or sometimes with, change of temperature (becoming cool), and with just an appreciable dulling of the tactile sensation ; there is also a slight loss of muscular sense. In a further state the hand is in contracture, becomes distinctly cold, and experiences more or less dulling of sensation. The loss of muscular sense is considerable. None of our subjects showed loss of sensation without contracture, except those who either had been or could be deeply hypnotized. Even in the fourth and fifth stages it was easier to produce loss of sensation if contracture had previously been induced.

CHAPTER VI

TREATMENT BY SUGGESTION

Introductory (Liébeault)—Repressions (with note on Freud, and examples of repressed complexes)—General principles of treatment, with Forels' list of diseases amenable to suggestion—Typical maladies (Hysteria—Neurasthenia—Obsessions—Insomnia—Nocturnal enuresis—Alcoholism—Morphinomania—Sex disorders, such as masturbation—Primary vaginismus—Spasmodic dysmenorrhœa—Absence of sex feeling — Nervousness — Sea-sickness — Chorea — Insanity—Constipation—Nervous Diarrhœa—Spasmodic asthma—Epilepsy)—Anæsthesia—Closing Note.

I. Introductory.

THE chief practical interest of hypnotism lies in its use as a therapeutic agent. Liébeault of Nancy first drew the attention of the medical world to the subject, and it is to the Nancy school, created by his work, that we really owe most of what we know of its practical applications, as well as the most widely accepted theoretical views of its nature.

Few men, I think, have shown such real heroism as the once humble doctor of Nancy. He commenced his professional career as a country practitioner, and in 1860 began to study hypnotism and to use it in his practice. In 1864 he removed to Nancy, and specialized in hypnotism, giving ·his services quite·

gratuitously to the poor, and living himself on the small private means which he possessed. For two years he worked hard at his first book on the subject, to be rewarded by the sale of only a single copy. But in 1882 he happened to effect a cure in a case of sciatica which had baffled Professor Bernheim for years. This brought Bernheim to see his practice, and what he saw made him a warm admirer and an enthusiastic follower. It speaks wonders for the pioneer that all those years he never faltered, but went on quietly with his work, unrecognized, unrewarded, regarded half-contemptuously by other members of his profession as a kind of crank. But Liébeault worked not for himself, but for his beloved poor, and their gratitude and affection were his sufficient and only reward. From the date of Bernheim's conversion began Liébeault's rise to fame, and after his death his name was added to the roll of honour of his most distinguished countrymen by the Government of France. He was a great man, the nobility of whose character surpassed even the value of his work.

Though I had studied hypnotism some years previously, it was at his clinic that I first saw it employed therapeutically. Medical men of every nation went to him to learn, and all were welcomed. Among others, Dr. Lloyd Tuckey went to see the famous clinic, and, impressed by his experience, he commenced treatment by suggestion in London. Later on, Dr. Milne Bramwell, who had used hypnotism with great success in his practice at Goole, came up to town and devoted himself to this kind of work alone. But the treatment at first met with strong opposition in this country, and still has many adversaries here. Of these, however, few seem to have really studied the subject, and many have never even seen a patient hypnotized. It is to Lloyd Tuckey's perseverance and Bramwell's determination and courage in advocating the claims of the new treatment that hypnotism chiefly owes its recognition in England as a legitimate addition to our armoury of healing.

Of course, it is impossible in a work like this to give more than a mere sketch of the results of treatment by suggestion, and altogether impossible to give a complete list of the different kinds of ailments which are said to have been benefited in this way. At present we do not know the limits of its usefulness, and it seems probable that it may yet be found to influence maladies to which at present it has not even been applied. But one may easily claim too much for it, and so bring it into discredit. It is an adjunct to medicine which is highly important, because certain types of disease appear to be amenable to it that can scarcely be influenced at all by other means, and because it can reinforce other more usual remedies by creating and maintaining a healthy condition of mind.

II. Repressions.

Since the days of Liébeault there have been great changes in the practice of dealing with mental cases, due to the advent of the discoveries of Professor Sigmund Freud, of Vienna. It is not too much to say that the theories which he evolved have revolutionized almost every branch of psychotherapeutics. Originally the aim of treatment was the removal of symptoms. Nowadays we can often remove the actual cause of the symptoms and so ensure their disappearance. Whereas a cure directed to the removal of symptoms was only too apt to be transient, one directed towards the eradication of the underlying cause is permanent.

It is to Freud that we owe our knowledge of these concealed phenomena. He it was who first pointed out that many nervous, mental, and even physical symptoms owe their origin to what are termed repressed memories. It is important to understand what is meant by a repressed memory, and perhaps an experience of my own may make it clear.

Like many others, a friend of mine received during the war a tremendous shock, so painful that he could not bear to think of it. He soon found that if anything tended to remind him of it, he experienced an intense emotion of horror before the memory of the actual event was anything like realized, and at once he voluntarily turned his thoughts away and refused to think of the subject. Soon this turning away became instinctive, and the result then of being reminded of the event was an immediate emotion of horror, followed at once by an instinctive, half-conscious withholding from all thought of the incident. It was much like knowing that a picture was there and refusing to look at it. Eventually the emotion of horror when aroused acted as a kind of danger signal. He seemed to feel rather than know what was coming, that the incident which gave rise to it was on the verge of being fully remembered; but he instantly repressed it, and drove it out of his mind. What struck me chiefly was the enormous strength of the remembered emotion compared with the extreme weakness of the memory of the incident. The emotion he could not prevent; the memory of the event he could repress quite easily.

Whilst in adult life very few can repress a memory completely, in child life the experience appears to be much more easy. I imagine that a child who has passed through some really painful experience reacts in much the same way as my friend did. When reminded of it he experiences at once the emotion, and pushes the incident out of his mind. But with constant repetition this process may, in the child, become completely automatic. If anything tends to recollection of the incident, the emotion arises first, and, instantly and automatically, the memory of the occurrence is repressed.

The result is that in after life, should anything tend to remind him of the incident, he will at once be seized by the emotion (which he cannot repress), but will remain in complete ignorance of its cause, since the memory of the latter is automatically repressed. The emotion will constitute a symptom ; and hence we see that the symptoms induced by a repressed memory are simply the recalled emotions, sensations, or impulses which occurred with the original incident. In the case of a simple, uncomplicated repression, if the sufferer can be made to recall to consciousness the original event, the whole of the symptoms caused by it vanish, and, as the examples which I give below show, vanish immediately—practically in a moment of time.

The newly recalled memory, which is often intensely vivid, at once takes its place among the ordinary painful memories, and behaves like them in that they produce no unpleasant symptoms. Like these, too, it begins gradually to fade away, until eventually it remains a mere dim recollection, harmless, and scarcely even painful, as the lapse of time gradually weakens it.

Other cases are not so simple. In the unconscious, in which these repressed memories exist, there is conclusive evidence that mental processes go on of which we are absolutely unaware, and new associations and grouping of ideas may arise, which may cause new symptoms apart from those caused by the simple repression of individual incidents. So it often happens that the symptoms do not correspond with the original experience, but with some new idea or system of ideas which, though connected with the incident, have begun entirely in the unconscious.

It will be convenient here to remind the reader of Freud's three divisions of consciousness, mentioned in a former chapter, firstly, the *conscious*, the ordinary consciousness of everyday life; secondly, the *pre-conscious*, wherein lie the memories that can be normally revived; and thirdly, the *unconscious*, which contains those memories which cannot be recalled by normal means.

In order to unravel these obscure memories the process of psycho-analysis invented by Freud is at present the only means we possess. It depends largely on dream analysis, and free association; but I would refer the reader to the many works published on the subject for further information as to its scope and methods. Unfortunately, it is necessarily a cumbrous and tedious process, and the time which it takes to carry out—often a year, or even two or more—and the concomitant expense, render it a method of treatment which can be indulged in only by comparatively wealthy and leisured people. The vast majority of these sufferers must, in the present state of our knowledge, be content to bear their ills unrelieved as best they may.

Happily, in many instances, repressed memories can be recovered by mere suggestion under hypnosis. Freud himself at one time used hypnotism for this purpose, but gave it up, partly, at any rate, on the ground that so few patients could be hypnotized. I presume he meant *deeply* hypnotized, for over 90 per cent. of persons can be readily hypnotized to some degree.

With the exception of some cases, of shell shock treated most successfully by Professor Brown, of King's College, I can find no record of cases of repression treated by hypnotism. It is perhaps owing to the introduction of psycho-analysis that so little attention seems to have been paid of late years to the possibilities of the use of hypnotism for treating repression; and no real advance seems to have been made in the practice of hypnotism for quite a number of years. No doubt this is partly due to the years of the Great War.

Yet if the knowledge of hypnotism is not to remain stagnant, it is clear that fresh investigation as to methods must be pursued, and it seems a pity that so much material should be wasted owing to there being at present no centre connected with the London medical schools, where studies may be carried on to determine how far suggestion is of use as a substitute for psycho-analysis. The question is of extreme importance, for, if a method of dealing with repression under hypnotism were discovered, hundreds of sufferers, for whom psycho-analysis is a practical impossibility, might be relieved.

Some seven years ago I determined to try whether these repressions could not be recalled under *light* hypnotism, and I found to my surprise that this was possible in quite a number of cases.

The method is very simple. I assume (and I believe it to be true) that the symptom from which the patient is suffering is identical in nature (though not in intensity) with an emotion, sensation, or impulse, which occurred at the time of the original event. I also assume that the occurrence gave rise to mental distress.

It must be clearly realized that the intensity of the symptom may far exceed that of the original counterpart which gave rise to it. Thus, there seems to be no limit to the intensity of pain caused by a repressed memory. In one of the cases cited below, a blow on the head inflicted by a little girl on her brother æt. four, who happened at the time to be in a state of great mental distress, caused agonizing pain some twenty-four years later, though the pain vanished immediately and permanently when the incident was recalled to his memory.

Acting on these assumptions, I suggest to the patient under hypnosis that he will recall an incident which aroused sensations exactly corresponding with those from which he suffers, though not necessarily of the same degree of intensity, and that at the time he suffered real mental distress. In a large proportion of cases the memory is then recalled, and the symptoms associated with it vanish immediately.

I do not for one moment pretend that in complicated cases, where intricate changes in association have occurred in the unconscious, that the mere unearthing of a repressed memory as here described is sufficient to effect a cure. In such cases, psycho-analysis is the only procedure likely to give relief.

The use of the method described above is confined to cases of simple repression, where no very complicated changes have taken place in the unconscious realm. But in quite a number of patients the mere unearthing of a repression is followed by immediate and apparently permanent cure. ·

Occasionally I have come across cases who, under the influence of hypnotism, seem to be able not merely to remember the repression, but also to analyse for themselves their own mental condition. An instance of this is recorded in case 9.

I may point out that the Freudian school would regard the original incident, of which the repressed memory is recovered, as symbolic of something else, generally of some sex complex. I do not deny that this is possibly the case—although one of our greatest psychologists once told me that he believed this assumption was made merely in order to fit in the facts with the Freudian theory. But I am not competent myself to express an opinion on the point. What I wish to emphasize is that, whatever theory we may hold as to the why and wherefore, the simple recalling of a repressed memory may, and often does, effect a permanent cure of the symptoms.

The following ten cases are examples of symptoms cured by the recovery of repressed memories which had caused them :

1. A lady, *æt.* 32. She was a woman the reverse of

hysterical, and of quite exceptional intellect. All her life, ever since she could remember, she had suffered intense fear on meeting other people. Even when walking in the street, she was attacked by this fear, caused by others coming towards her. The fear was always accompanied by a feeling of strong pressure on the back of her head. She was, in consequence of this, quite unable to go into society. In addition she had a terror of going into any big building, though small buildings did not affect her. Besides these two symptoms, she constantly fancied that she heard people saying unpleasant things about her. The terror of big buildings appeared to have arisen later than the other fears. I saw her about ten times. The fear of meeting people and the hearing of people talking about her originated at such an early age that I had to get her to recall the events of her babyhood, and she eventually remembered herself in long clothes. We were able to verify one or two of the incidents which she recollected at that early age as having actually occurred.

The fear of meeting people and the pressure on the back of the head was due to repressed memory of having her face washed as a baby. Apparently the process terrified her very much, and at last she became afraid that anyone who approached her was going to wash her face. Of course, she had really been most ungently handled at this early period of her life.

The pressure on the back of her head was caused by

the hand of the nurse holding her head during the washing. When she realised this, she exclaimed: "Now I know what the pain is at the back of my nose. It is the soapsuds getting into my nostrils." I had not been told previously of this symptom.

The origin of her fear of big buildings was explained in this way. Her mother was fond of playing on the church organ, and one day, when between three and four years old, she accompanied her. She was perfectly happy until the people began to come in for service, but was then seized with terror and the feeling of pressure on her head. The incident alarmed her so much that she repressed the memory of it. So that in this instance the event which was repressed was actually caused by the earlier repression of having her face washed. The moment she recollected these repressions, the symptoms due to them vanished, and have now ceased for nearly a year.

The third symptom, that of hearing people talking about her, I have not yet removed, as she was obliged to leave town. However, I have no doubt that two or three more trials will suffice to get rid of it, for we know to what it was due, only the exact details being as yet unrevealed. But I am precluded from giving an account of the fact of the repression, which has already been unearthed, for reasons which would be of no interest to the reader.

2. A lady, æt. 31. Highly educated. Engaged in educational work.

For ten years she had suffered from an intense

craving for alcohol, which, however, she had always successfully resisted. At first I thought it might be a form of true dipsomania; but it presented characteristics which were so much unlike it, that I thought it might be due to some repressed memory.

I saw her twice. On the first occasion I hypnotized her very lightly. She was only just in the first stage and could not open her eyes. I suggested that she would recall some incident of childhood which was connected with drink or drunkenness, and which had distressed her greatly. I told her it had probably occurred between the ages of three and five.

However, she could recall nothing; so I roused her and told her to come again the next morning. Five minutes later she returned, to tell me that she had recalled the incident. It appeared that, when she was about three years old, a man had told her mother in her presence about a woman who had got drunk and murdered her own child. The story had distressed her intensely for some days, and then seems to have been repressed. The craving was really not a craving at all, but a fear lest she should take alcohol and some tragic result should follow. When she had told me what she remembered, I said to her: "Don't you ever feel afraid of injuring your pupils?" She replied: "Yes—and I can't think why." This symptom was of course due to the murder of the child. The symptoms left her, and she has been well for some four years.

3. A little girl, æt. about 14. She had been at

various boarding-schools, but was unable to remain in them owing to constant vomiting, although she was quite well the moment she got into the train to go home. She was fond of her school life and distressed at being unable to remain.

She had been in the hands of various medical men, and had amongst other things undergone a course of Weir Mitchell treatment in a nursing home, but no improvement whatever resulted. It seemed probable that it was repressed memory of nausea or vomiting.

I saw her only once. Under light hypnosis I suggested that she would recall some forgotten incident of early childhood, probably between the ages of three and five, which had caused her great distress and made her feel very sick. She immediately began to retch; and I asked her whether she remembered. She said "Yes," and I hurriedly aroused her, as she was apparently about to vomit.

The repressed memory was as follows. Her father was an antiquarian, and among other curiosities he kept a mummy in the house. This she could never be persuaded to see, and she seems to have been really afraid to look at it.

One day, when she was rather more than three years old, her little sister said to her: "Come and look at the mummy," and she refused. This part of the incident, however, it afterwards transpired, was not repressed, as she had remembered it in her ordinary life. The rest of the incident was repressed. Her sister then said: "If I give you sixpence will you come?" and to this she assented. Having safely obtained possession of the sixpence, she promptly refused to go, to the natural indignation of her sister, who insisted that, as she had taken the sixpence, she must come. She then did go and looked at the mummy, and was sick when she saw it.

No symptoms, however, appeared until she went to school. Then after a time vomiting commenced, and if, as usually happened, it began in the morning, it continued more or less all day.

On one afternoon when she had been free all day, she was compelled against her will to take part in a game (I think it was cricket), which she dreaded and did her best to evade. However, she had to play, and at once began vomiting. Probably being compelled to play a game she feared reminded her of being compelled to look at the mummy. I found that the attacks, which began when she woke in the morning and lasted all day, were preceded by dreams of mummies—often of being chased by a mummy. From that day to this, though she is at a boarding-school, she has never again vomited, or even once suffered from nausea.

4. In the case following I was aware of what the repression was. The patient was totally unable to recall it although he had been informed of the incident, and I therefore set myself to the task of reviving the concealed memory. The result was a complete cure.

Mr. S., æt. 37. He had suffered from fits from the

age of five until he was twelve years old. Some of the
fits appear to have been of the nature of petit mal—
but some were clearly grand mal, several happening
during the week sometimes, occasionally occurring
during his sleep with involuntary enuresis. At the
age of twelve they ceased entirely.

Eventually the patient got work in India, and there
suffered much from intense domestic worries.

Two years before he came to me his fits returned,
but they had changed in character. He would
suddenly become unconscious, and would remain
unconscious sometimes for as long as two hours.
I have no doubt they were cataleptic. I found from
what his mother told me that at the age of five he
had been much terrified by a dog watching over her
puppies, which had run out of a house as he was passing
and barked furiously at him, though it did not attack
him. Twenty minutes later he was said to have
become suddenly unconscious; but I could get no
reliable data as to the duration of this first attack,
and about a week later he had a fit—which seems to
have resembled petit mal, as it lasted for some minutes.
This attack (as well as several others) he was
made to recall under hypnosis, and he recollected
"thinking of nothing" as he stood in the hall, and
being led up to his nursery in that condition. I found
that though he could recall events both previous to,
and immediately subsequently to, the dog incident, of
this he had no recollection whatever; nor could he
recall it by any effort of memory.

It seemed so probable that in some way his symptoms were due to a repressed memory of the event that I determined to try to recover it.

Another fact made it still more certain that the incident was repressed, and not forgotten. Though he lives in the town where the episode took place, the houses in the street where it happened were always unfamiliar to him, though he frequently passed them. The following extracts from an account of his case written by himself will give an idea of his condition when I saw him:

"I saw Dr. Wingfield in 1918 on the following dates: July 11th and 17th, August 6th and 7th, September 16th, 17th, 18th, 19th, 20th, 21st, and October 2nd and 3rd.

"Before seeing him I was suffering from depression, nearly continuous, but at times becoming more severe. Whilst under his treatment the fits of depression became gradually more marked and latterly very severe, but between times I was more normal. Before seeing him I used to have a haunted feeling out of doors (in——ton only), especially if I was alone. It was a sense of some impalpable presence, or a little black devil following me at a distance of a few feet behind me, and at about the height of my shoulder. After my first visit to Dr. Wingfield this did not recur, but was replaced by a marked nervous_ ness in streets, especially at crossings, which was very intense towards September 16th, after which it became very slight..

" I had from time to time suffered from unexplained attacks of vomiting, which became particularly frequent at the beginning of September, but ceased in the middle of that month. This was always in the evening before bedtime. I have had no cataleptic fit since my first visit to Dr. Wingfield. . . .

" My first two visits to Dr. Wingfield in July produced very little effect—as I was a difficult subject to hypnotize. On August 6th, whilst under hypnosis, I noticed that in my recollection of the houses near where the dog was, there was a misty gap, extending some three houses before the dog-house, and double that number beyond. During the period between August 6th and 27th, my recollection of the houses became gradually clearer, the gap consisting only of the dog's house and three houses beyond.

" On August 27th, under hypnosis, I remembered facts of my first fit as a child, and the iron railings in front of the dog's house.

" Between August 27 and September 16th, I got a clearer recollection of the houses, and the white mist became lighter with a more substantial centre. I also recollected further details of my first attack as a child.

" On September 16th, under hypnosis, the previously recollected incidents became clearer, and on the following day, under hypnosis, I first saw my father running towards me when the dog came at me, and subsequently I recollected the house extremely clearly, but with only a faint mist where the dog should have been. After this at night I used to get short glimpses of the dog, usually its hindquarters, sometimes a bit of its flank. During this period I recollected most of my first attack except its start. On September 19th, I clearly associated my attacks of vomiting as a child with fear. For some nights I suffered considerably from fear. On the 27th I heard one or two faint barks under hypnosis.

"On September 28th, I experienced considerable fear just as I was passing the house where the dog had lived, but this was not repeated when I passed the house on October 1st. Between September 21st and October 2nd, I got an extremely foggy impression of the outline of the dog standing in the doorway. On October 2nd, I felt intense fear for the first time under hypnosis; and the fear lasted an hour or two afterwards. Whilst under hypnosis I very clearly saw the dog on the occasion of my attack in India in 1914, and then in my first attack in England, and last attack in England in the order named. Any sign of recollection of the dog in the house was at once obliterated by the dog as it appeared in my attack in India. I heard a few distinct faint barks. On the night of October 2nd I felt fear, which at times became very acute for a few minutes.

"On October 3rd, I clearly recollected, under hypnosis, the dog as the cause of my first attack when a child. I then clearly recollected the dog standing in the doorway, and heard her bark."

At this last trial he told me that he had seen the

dog precisely, barking and running out at him. On October 2nd, he told me that he saw the dog in the doorway, and outside at the gate—but that fear seemed to prevent him from seeing her actually running out. During treatment he adds : " My memory seemed to advance only when under hypnosis, and at night between going to bed and going to sleep."

On October 14th, he writes : " I have suffered less from depression, and what depression I have experienced during the last few days has been much less intense than formerly—in fact, altogether in a different class. I have lost all fear in crossing a street, and now feel perfectly normal.

" The memory of the dog incident has now become quite an ordinary memory of a distant event, though for two or three days it was continually with me, only as a memory it is true, but a memory of something recent.

" I have been thinking over my continual failure to remember what my thoughts were during any attack, and I wonder whether it was that both my conscious and subconscious self were paralyzed by the fear, and I really had no thoughts to remember. This would seem to explain why, in some attacks, I could remain on my feet, and even walk away, when the stimulus was provided to the muscles by someone leading me, as in my first attack."

In a further note the patient says :

" I have recollected seeing the dog in four of my

attacks, namely, the first attack I had as a child, an attack in India in 1914, my first attack in England in 1917, and my last attack in England in 1918.

" In each case the dog appeared at exactly the same angle to me. During the first attack in England in 1917 it appeared on my right-hand side, the only possible place for it to appear from the position in which I was sitting, but in all the other cases it appeared on my left-hand side, which was the side on which it was when it actually attacked me. In the Indian attack the dog stood out more clearly than in the other attacks, which is only natural from the position at the edge of the circle of firelight in the dark forest at night. In each attack the dog appeared motionless, not in the position of a stationary dog, but in a position of action, such as might be registered by an instantaneous photograph. On first seeing the dog in these attacks, I jumped to the conclusion that the activity indicated was the position of barking, because I knew that it was by barking that the dog had terrified me. But since I have made further progress in seeing the actual attack, I am convinced that the position of the dog in the attacks is the instant after she had jumped to her feet, and before she rushed forward barking—that is, the instant immediately before she uttered the first bark, and immediately before the point where the most intense terror arose."

Since then the patient has been free from fits and terrors. It is unfortunate that he had no more time at his disposal, for I do not know what the connection was between the dog and the little black devil and the phobia of crossing the street—if there was any.

As these symptoms all disappeared without any suggestion being made that they would do so, it seems most probable that they were connected with the dog incident; but only a longer and more searching analysis would have shown what it was. The only suggestions made at any time were that he should remember the attacks made by the dog, and secondly, that he should recollect his fits.

5. A schoolboy, *æt.* 12½. He suffered from intense terror of the dark. The terror had commenced about two years before I saw him, and had become intolerable. Not only were the nights terrible, but the days also, because he knew the night was coming. He had been quite unable to sleep in a room by himself.

There was a history that when he was five years old he had slept for a week in the same room with a new governess, who was then discovered to be insane. His parents became aware at the time that something had terrified him during that week, but they could never get from him any account of what had occurred, and when he came to me I found him quite unable to recollect anything about it, or even what his governess looked like. As it seemed more than likely that his fear of the dark was due to a repressed memory of something which had then occurred, I determined to try to make him recall it.

His parents had some time before taken the boy to

see an eminent physician, who pronounced the cheerful verdict that the boy was injured for life, and that nothing whatever could be done for him.

I treated him five times, and on the fifth trial he recalled the cause of his terrors.

The governess, who was a Roman Catholic, used to wake him in the night, put a crucifix into his hands, and tell him to hold it tight, as the whole room was full of devils, who were going to attack them. She prayed hysterically, and every now and then would point to the shadows, saying she saw some terrible being or other, which she used apparently to describe more or less, one being a man like a Chinaman. . Naturally, the unfortunate child passed through extremities of terror.

His memories revived a little with each trial after the first, and the night after the fourth treatment he suffered from frightful nightmare. He could not remember what it was in the morning, but told his mother he would recall it when I saw him; and it turned out that the nightmare was a recollection of his week of terror. When I saw him the day after, his memory had been revived; he said he felt quite different, and no longer felt the old fear.

In cases of this kind, however, when the fear is destroyed, there almost always arises a new fear—that is, a fear lest the old fear should arise. In this case, it was a fear lest, if he went into the dark, the old terror should recur.

This "fear of a fear" which is, after all, quite a

reasonable one, is destroyed by time, and by the constantly repeated discovery that even in the dark the old fear does not recur, however much he dreads that it may. With this boy the " fear of a fear " lasted a few weeks and then vanished entirely. To use his own words, he now " likes the night as much as the day."

6. Schoolboy, *æt.* 14.

Boarded at a public school. He had been suffering for two years ˗from great home-sickness, which had become so severe, and interfered so seriously with his school life, that the question of removing him was raised.

I found on questioning him that two years previously he had been slightly bullied, and ever since had experienced an almost constant feeling of apprehensive dread. He felt that something terrible was threatening him, though he had no idea as to its nature.

The repression was· unearthed at the fifth attempt. When twenty-two months old he had eaten orange peel, and, in order to punish him, his nurse had shut him up either behind a dark curtain or in a cupboard. This terrified him, and he was frightened lest she should do it again, and appears to have repressed the memory of the incident. I have no doubt that being bullied had tended to remind him of this incident.

When he recalled it I said to him : " Is that what you were afraid of ?" " Yes," he replied, " of course it is." " Why ' of course ' ?" I asked. " You only knew of it first this moment." "I know that; but I know that is what it was," was the answer.

I asked him whether he felt his apprehension, and he said that it was entirely gone. He returned to school, but has been ever since perfectly well of his home-sickness, and his house-master has told me that he is quite a different boy. He has been well for about twenty months.

7. A soldier, *æt.* 27. He had been invalided out of the Army on account of extreme phobia. He was first terrified of the dark, and then terrified of being alone even during the day, and was unable to go about unless accompanied. I treated him only once. Under hypnosis I suggested that he would remember an incident of his childhood when he was terrified and in darkness. He at once had a kind of nightmare, and I roused him. He recollected, when he was, he thought, about two or four, that he was accidentally locked in a cellar, and he remembered his frantic attempts at escape and how he made his hands raw by beating at the door.

Instantly he felt well and said he knew he would be all right alone. I saw him eight days later. He came alone, and said that the phobia had left him entirely.

8. Another soldier suffered from nearly identical symptoms. He was terrified of being alone; but it did not appear that it had made any difference whether it was night or day. He, too, had to have an escort, as he was quite unable to go about by himself.

Under hypnosis he recalled how, as a small child, he had got separated from his parents at one of the great exhibitions, and had been lost for three hours. As in the previous case, the phobia vanished at once. I saw him about a week later, and he told me that on the evening of the day on which first I saw him he had been able to go home by himself quite happily, the first time he had been able to do so since his illness. Unfortunately I lost sight of him, and do not know how he went on afterwards.

9. A professional man, about 30 years of age. He had been obliged to get leave from his work on account of his illness three years before he came to me. When I first saw him he was dangerously depressed, for he had begun to believe that he would never recover.

His malady began as follows : Three years before he noticed that, if he put on a loose collar, he got pain over the region of his appendix. Eventually he was unable to wear his collars tight enough, the pain got higher up, and he began to suffer from vomiting, intense depression, and a feeling of overwhelming shame. When I saw him he was in despair of ever getting well. The case occurred some seven years ago, and I had had but little experience of this method of treatment, which I was first beginning to study.

At first I found that under light hypnosis he could recall nothing in connection with his trouble. I then suggested under hypnosis : " Dream. You will dream of something connected with your condition." On my asking him what he saw, he said, " A big mirror."

For some days I got no further, and then he recollected that the mirror in question used to stand in the bathroom of his old home. This put me on the right track, for in a bathroom he would see himself naked. Eventually, after many trials, lasting nearly three weeks, he unravelled the enigma.

It seems that as a small boy he thought he was malformed, and the idea became repressed.

An incident tended to remind him of this. When he put on a loose collar and went out into the air, his neck felt cold and uncovered. This had given rise to a subconscious feeling of absolute nakedness. When asked under hypnosis what he felt when he had on a loose collar, he exclaimed: " Oh, I am quite naked. Everyone can see I am malformed." The pain was quite a secondary affair. During an attack of nakedness-horror he seems to have suffered real pain over the arm, owing, I suppose, to some transient ailment, and ever after with each attack of depression it recurred as a memory pain.

There had been no improvement in his condition until the final trial; but then he became well immediately, went straight back to his work, and has had no recurrence of any kind of distress since.

10. The following case is of interest as showing that in certain cases a repressed memory can be recovered and the symptoms caused by it stopped and then re-repressed, with the result that the symptoms immediately recur. I am unfortunately precluded

10

from giving all the details of this extraordinary case; but must content myself with an outline.

Mr. F., *æt.* 28, came to me for excessive smoking, desiring help to enable him to give it up. I discovered later that he had twice previously (once six years and once six months before) nearly killed himself by taking an overdose of a poison which I shall call chloral. He returned a week after my first interview. He had largely reduced his smoking, but now complained of agonizing pain between his shoulders. I found I could remove it at once by suggestion, but it always recurred within twenty-four hours. One day he told me that he felt he must do something, but he did not know what it was. Clearly this was an impulse probably due to some unconscious repression.

I hypnotized him, and he passed at once into deep hypnosis. In fact, I was never able to hypnotize him lightly, deep hypnosis always appearing immediately.

I then asked him what it was he had to do. "Sums," was the answer. When I inquired why he had to do sums, I found he had now passed back to his childhood days, and he told me why he was so distressed. I then asked him what caused the pain, and he replied: "Oh, Mary has hit me in the back with a croquet mallet." I told him he would recollect this on awakening, roused him, and found that he remembered perfectly. It appears that at the age of four when he was in great distress over his sums, his little sister Mary had indeed hit him in the back with a croquet mallet. The pain was gone, and never recurred again. The patient had many repressed memories, each having its own peculiar symptom, and with recovery of each repression the corresponding symptom disappeared.

But I soon discovered that he had a dual personality. I found eventually that, during many years, he had blanks of memory, and that, when I hypnotized him, I really called up this second personality. Under hypnosis his behaviour was quite different from that of a normal individual. He would not accept any suggestions unless he approved of them, and would argue the point when I tried to get him to do so. In fact, all I could do was to use persuasion when he was hypnotized.

The hypnotic personality, unlike that of the normal man, had assumed the power of criticism, and this always seems to me one of the main differences between the ordinary unconsciousness of the normal man and a true second personality. Once the subconscious assumes the power of criticism, it takes on the function of a real second personality.

One symptom from which he suffered frequently was vomiting. This I found was due to a memory of having been made to vomit when he had taken chloral, as mentioned above. Then came the question—why did he take the chloral? This was due to a trifling incident of childhood, when he was about four years old, and one which was completely repressed and very difficult to recover. He had a cold, and his mother gave him some medicine. It made him feel better, and he asked for more ; but his mother had said, "No, you can't have any more : its poison."

The only poison which he knew of was chloral. A conflict was then set up between his desire to take his medicine, which he identified as chloral, and his fear of doing so. This became painful, and he repressed it. Even now he represses the memories of recent events with extraordinary ease.

Some twenty-two years later the unconscious conflict seems to have re-awakened, and this time the idea that he would take his medicine (chloral) got the upper hand. He was seized with an irresistible impulse, bought some chloral, and took it, and was with difficulty saved from death. Some five-and-a-half years later the same thing occurred. I had discovered that frequently his second personality had an intense desire to possess chloral, and I found that he had occasional blanks of memory, and that, during the period which was obliterated from his mind, he almost always had managed to purchase chloral, though he did not take it. I found, too, that the periods of longing to get it were always marked by vomiting; but that so long as he remembered the incident about the medicine neither vomiting nor desire for chloral occurred. But frequently he could not recall the incident: it was re-repressed, and the vomiting at once recurred.

I asked his second personality why he had forgotten the incident one day, and the reply was : "Because I wanted to forget it." Asked why he wanted to forget it, he said : "Because I can't get my poison if I remember it." Another repression, giving rise to different symptoms, which was recalled, was one day re-repressed, and the symptom at once recurred, though it vanished permanently when I made him recall the repression for the second time.

I have never met with or heard of any other case where a recovered repressed memory was re-repressed, and the instance is a very striking one; the re-repression always resulting immediately in a return of the corresponding symptoms.

What I tried to do in this case was to fuse his two personalities. I used to try to persuade him, whilst under hypnosis, to remember when he was awake all that he remembered under hypnosis, but was always met with a point-blank refusal, and I never could get him to consent to do so under any conditions. The case is therefore, so far as the dual personality goes, uncured; nor do I see any way by which the second personality may be conquered. The dual personality had been in existence for many years when I first saw him; but I have reason for hoping that it will never again wish to take chloral.

11. In only one case have I known a relapse. The case was that of a lady, *æt.* 21, who had for six years suffered from terror in church, and, if alone, in the street.

She recalled an incident when she was a child. She had read a story in which the heroine went suddenly mad, and was hurried off to an asylum, and this had horrified her greatly. I found that she often dreamed that she had gone mad, and was seized by attendants to be carried off to an asylum. Her terror in the street—which vanished at once—was probably due to an idea that she would go mad, and that people in the street were ready to hurry her off in the same way. But the terror of church I could not remove. She afterwards married, and when, three years later, she had her second child, she nursed it when she was quite unfit to do so, and became exceedingly run down. The fear of being alone in the street again recurred. I saw her, but on that occasion failed to discover the mental cause of her relapse, and since then I have not heard of her.

I think it is likely that the memory of the story was not the original repression, but I do not know.

Sometimes when I could not make the patient recall the repression directly, I have succeeded in making him, or her, dream, under actual hypnosis, of something connected with it, and in this way eventually discovered what I sought. Thus, in case 9 the patient dreamed that he saw a big mirror, and at last recalled that it had stood in the bathroom of his old home. In another, a lady who suffered from intense pain in the left side of her face, dreamt under hypnosis that she saw a glass of water standing on a table. This enabled her a few days later to recall the whole experience—an unfortunate love affair. The man to whom she was attached had drunk half a tumblerful of water, and, when she was alone, she had drunk the rest. In another case, of which I have unfortunately lost the notes, the patient was a lady who suffered from three symptoms. She had frequently hysterical clenching of her left hand, due to her having crushed a letter, which caused her great distress, in her left hand. She also suffered from great depression and a longing for death, and when this was most marked, she would often hear a voice saying, "Kill yourself, kill yourself," and she fancied she smelt a strong odour of smoke.

The incident of the clenched hand she recalled, so far as I can recollect, on the second trial, but I could not arouse the memory of the incidents which caused the other two. I therefore suggested that she would dream of some incident connected with the symptoms, and she dreamt she saw the name of a theatre (I think it was Prince's) in red letters, on a white ground. On the fourth or fifth trial she saw the words "Prince's Theatre." This resulted in her recalling a few days later the following incident:

A few days after getting news of the death in action, during the South African War, of a young man to whom she was much attached, she was crossing a London street. She came to a street refuge where, luckily, there happened to be a policeman, and was going to walk straight on. The policeman seized her by the arm, and dragged her back, saying rather angrily, "You'll kill yourself one day." She then saw that she had only just avoided being run over by an omnibus, which was emitting a good deal of smoke, and on which was an advertisement with the words " Prince's Theatre " upon it. She recovered, but died of pneumonia two years later.

I have, I fear, tired the reader by treating of these cases at such length ; but I regard them as the most important that we have to treat. They are demonstrations that there is great scope for improvement in the methods used, and I hope that one day we may be able successfully to treat many of the patients who at present could be treated by psycho-analysis alone, but who are precluded by practical considerations from ever attempting the process.

Professor Brown of King's College has used hypnotism most successfully in cases of so-called war shock, to enable the patients to recall the horrors which overcame them, and the results have been most striking.

III. General Principles of Treatment.

Until a few years ago, most physicians who made use of hypnotism aimed at inducing as deep a stage as possible. But of late few do so, the lighter stages being as a rule quite sufficient for therapeutic purposes.

Moll long ago pointed out that the real dangers are two in number : viz., the increased tendency to hypnosis, and the heightened susceptibility to suggestion in the waking state, both of which he believes are avoidable. Many critics of hypnotism, however, have insisted that repeated hypnosis—at any rate, deep hypnosis—has these drawbacks. .

Fortunately, in the vast majority of cases which come for treatment, deep hypnosis is quite unnecessary. In my own practice I have, except on very rare occasions for special reasons, never induced the deep state for many years.

I sometimes make suggestions under quite light hypnosis, or else use Bramwell's method, which, when it acts, seems to be much the same thing; but most frequently I combine both methods, by first inducing light hypnosis, and then suggesting to the patient that he will not attend to me, but fix his mind on some restful train of thought whilst I make suggestions. I find in this way that I get results more rapidly than I do when I use Bramwell's method alone. Even if the patient cannot help attending to me, I find that the effect of a suggestion is apparent even on the first day of treatment. During the war I saw a good many cases of insomnia amongst soldiers, and in every case they slept on the night after the first suggestion had been made.

Moll, though he advised as deep a hypnosis as possible, points out that it is a mistake to suppose that the light stages have no value, and Liébeault, though he insisted that the best results were obtained in deep sleep, says "much depended on the suggestibility of the subject." For example, A may be as susceptible to suggestion in the light state as B is in the deep one, and experience has convinced me of the truth of this.

I may say here that, though in years gone by I

frequently did make use of deep hypnosis, I have never seen any sign of harm produced thereby; and Bramwell states that Forel asserted that neither he nor Liébeault, Bernheim, Wetherstrand, Van Eeden, Jung, Moll, or the other followers of the Nancy school had ever seen a single instance in which mental or physical harm had been caused by the use of suggestion in therapeutics. As the total number of their cases certainly exceeds fifty thousand, hypnotism obviously cannot be a very dangerous procedure.

Many complaints are amenable to suggestion. Forel gives the following list of diseases in which it has been found affectual :

Forel's List of Diseases Amenable to Suggestion.

Spontaneous somnambulism.

Pains of all description, especially headache, toothache which does not depend on abscess, etc.

Sleeplessness.

Functional paralyses and contractures.

Organic paralyses and contractures (as palliative means).

Chlorosis (results extremely favourable).

Disturbance of menstruation (metrorrhagia and amenorrhœa).

Loss of appetite and all nervous digestive disturbances.

Constipation and diarrhœa (provided that it does not depend on catarrh or fermentation).

Gastric and intestinal dyspepsia (including pseudo-dilatation).

Psychical impotence, pollutions, onanism, perverted sexual appetite and the like.

Alcoholism and morphinism (only by the suggestion of total abstinence).

Chronic muscular and arthritic rheumatism.

Lumbago.

The so-called neurasthénic disturbances.

Stammering; nervous disturbances of vision.

Blepharospasm.

Pavor nocturnus of children.

Sickness and sea-sickness, the vomiting of pregnancy.

Enuresis nocturna (often very difficult on account of the depth of the normal sleep).

Chorea.

Nervous attacks of coughing (also in emphysema).

Hysterical disturbances of all kinds, including hystero-epileptic attacks, anæsthesia, phobias, and the like.

Bad habits of all kinds.

All hypochondriacal paræsthesias, irritable weaknesses, conceptions of impulse and the like, are more difficult to cure.

Other authors give many other complaints as amenable to hypnotic suggestion, but it would serve no useful purpose to extend the list. Those enumerated above give a sufficient indication of the classes of maladies in which the treatment has been found successful. Most of these appear to be examples of functional neuroses in which no organic lesion can be found.

But it is unnecessary to give detailed accounts of the treatment of every. kind of disease amenable to treatment. I shall therefore confine myself to those maladies which most commonly occur, and which everyone who practises this form of treatment is most likely to meet.

IV. Typical Maladies.

1. *Hysteria.*—Bramwell records several cures, and Forel counts fifteen cures out of twenty-eight. When these patients can be hypnotized, especially if they pass into the deep sleep, prognosis as regards the removal of the symptoms is generally favourable. But often the patient relapses sometimes, as Tuckey points out, even during treatment after a temporary improvement. It appears to me that mere suggestion, though it may relieve the symptoms, cannot of itself cure the real underlying condition. For this purpose psycho-analysis is the only treatment which offers much reasonable hope; and it is to be regretted that for the majority of these sufferers it is, in practice, out of the question.

On this ground I do not advise hypnotism alone in a generalized hysterical condition, except as a means of alleviating the most distressing symptoms. But symptoms I have often succeeded in removing. Two cases are worth recording—one a case of hysterical deafness, and the other a case of hysterical blindness confined to the left eye.

Mrs. X., the wife of a sergeant-major, had become

stone deaf after her confinement four years before I saw her. She was sent to me by Mr. Yearsley.

When I first saw her she could hear no sound whatever, however loud, and her husband informed me that since the onset of her deafness she had become extremely irritable.

I wrote out the directions which I wished her to follow, telling her that I should ask her to lie down, that I should then close her eyes and make a few strokes over them, and that I should then make suggestions which she would hear, though possibly not consciously, and that when I roused her she would hear.

But she did not hear when I awakened her. However, when her husband brought her again he told me that half an hour after I had seen her, her hearing had suddenly returned, and that she had complained of the noise of the whistle of the engines during her homeward journey, and had understood what he said to her. Within an hour or two, however, the old condition returned.

Unfortunately, circumstances made it impossible for her to come to town more than once a week, except during one week when she came twice.

She gradually improved, and on the next occasion on which I saw her could hear fairly well. Her irritability of temper, too, was much less. On the third occasion she told me that though she could hear every word I said, she forgot it before I could utter the next, a rather interesting mental condition. It was remarkable, too, that for a long time after she could hear, she seemed afraid to trust herself, evidently uncertain whether her newly restored sense was a correct reporter.

She returned to India, and I was disappointed, though not surprised, to hear that her old condition had gradually returned, and that at the end of four months she was as deaf as before. It was unfortunate that she could be treated so seldom (I saw her only seven times), for one may fairly suppose that, had the treatment been given a fair chance, the result might have been more lasting.

The second case was that of a man *æt.* 47—a clerk. He was a patient at Moorfields Ophthalmic Hospital, and was sent to me by Mr. Grimsdale. For twenty-three years he had been almost totally blind in the left eye. He suffered great supra-orbital pain as well. Nothing wrong could be discovered by the ophthalmoscope, but as the eye caused so much pain and was apparently useless, the question of its removal had been raised. He had had a rather severe injury to his forehead previous to the onset of blindness, but there was nothing to account for his condition.

I saw him only four times ; but the result was satisfactory.

When he came to me he could just distinguish light from darkness when the right eye was covered. The vision of the right eye was defective owing to errors of refraction. I hypnotized him on the first occasion on which I saw him, and he passed immediately into deep sleep. Placing my hand over his left eye, I said :

" When you count ten you will wake, and when you wake you will see." I counted ten and he awoke; and at once exclaimed in tones of excitement : " I can see —I can see !" I then took him to a picture hanging on the wall, and told him to look at it. He said he could see it, but it was all misty. It reminded me forcibly of the account of the New Testament miracle —" seeing men as trees walking." Then I put my hand on his forehead and said : " Watch. It is getting clearer every moment. It is quite clear now." He could then see quite clearly, and on the last occasion on which he came, about a month later, his vision was still perfectly clear.

Another case, that of a lady who had for ten years refused all solid food, yielded at once to suggestion when I had persuaded her to tell me of the real origin of the mischief, an unfortunate love affair, though before I knew of this six trials had failed to effect any improvement. She now eats and drinks and enjoys life like other people.

2. *Neurasthenia.*—It is unfortunate that the meaning of the term neurasthenia has not been more exactly defined. Whatever its nature, it is a condition which, as a rule, presents a few more or less constant features.

There is generally wasting, the reflexes are exaggerated, and the pulse-rate is increased. Mentally, the power of concentration is impaired, depression is nearly always present, and the patient's thoughts usually run in a small and vicious circle, always coming round to himself and his illness; and this inability to take his thoughts off himself is, perhaps, the most distressing feature of the condition. The physical symptoms point to an increased katabolism, and the increased reflexes to a lowering of the resistances of the nervous system. I have often wondered whether the whole condition is not mainly physical, due simply to the breaking down of the nerve resistances. In such a condition one would expect an increase of efferent impulses, and the wasting and possibly the increased pulse-rate may be due to this. Again, the constantly reiterated depressing thoughts point to a lowered resistance in the tracts concerned in their production.

One would expect too, that, with the abnormal flow of neurokyme the reserves of nerve force would be much depleted, and perhaps its pressure or potential, to use an analogy, may be much diminished. Possibly ideas caused by cerebral currents of low pressure tend to be depressing ones.

It is at any rate certain that bromide in small doses does great good in these cases, and the chief action of bromide is to increase the resistances, and bring them more nearly to normal. Rest, too, by diminishing the flow of neurokyme may give time for the resistances to re-form, and a combination of rest with small doses of bromide may result in accumulating a certain reserve of nerve energy.

I find it difficult to believe that suggestion by itself can cure the condition, though it may help to alleviate some of the symptoms. Others, however, consider that suggestion may do much. Crichton Miller advocates its use, but personally I now trust in these cases to the more usual treatment by rest, bromides, and overfeeding, and use suggestion only to combat individual symptoms such as insomnia.

3. *Obsessions.*—Bramwell concludes, as the results of his great experience, that suggestion yields better results in cases of obsession than in any other class of functional nerve disorder.

In the majority of these patients, Bramwell says, the predominant element is fear. "Generally they dread that something is going to happen to them, such as sudden illness, death, or suicide, or they fear that they have actually injured others or may yield to an impulse to do so in one way or another."

Not a few of these cases are really suffering from the effects of repression, and these cannot be supposed to be really well until the irritating incident has been unrepressed.

In two cases of my own, who suffered from morbid fear lest something should happen to near relatives, the real cause was an unconscious desire for their death, which had been repressed, and the symptoms cleared away when the repression was unearthed. Many of the cases which I have seen appeared to have commenced by a sudden idea implanted at a moment when the patients were suffering from acute mental exhaustion, produced by worry. Thus, a lady who was intensely worried owing to circumstances induced by the war, took up a mat from the floor, and three

11

cockroaches ran out. Ever after she was obsessed by the fear that there were blackbeetles inhabiting every room that she entered, and later by the same fear with regard to spiders as well.

A common obsession is the fear that the patient either has cancer or will get it.

Most people suffer from some obsessional impulse, such as an inclination to avoid the cracks between the paving-stones, or to touch the iron railings with a stick. Sir George Savage, who notes this, states that he has himself this obsession to a certain extent. Many of these cases recover rapidly under treatment, but some are very difficult to cure.

Thus, one patient had for a year an obsessional fear that the police were seeking him. He had one day passed his water in the garden, and had then observed a maid at the window of a house overlooking it. The obsession increased to such an extent that he thought he heard everyone saying, " The police are after that man,'" and his life became utterly miserable. A week's treatment dispelled all his symptoms.

Another common obsessional fear is that of travelling in a train. I have had many cases of this, and all but two were cured. In every case of obsession I believe that hypnotism is worth a trial; and if it be due to a repression, it may sometimes be discovered and the patient cured.

4. *Insomnia.*—Though it is usually impossible to induce sleep at a moment's notice, unless the patient can be deeply hypnotized, a great many cases can be

induced to sleep by suggestions made under light hypnosis some hours before it is to take effect. A suggestion given in the morning or the afternoon that the patient will sleep that night usually succeeds. During the war I treated many soldiers suffering from insomnia in this way, and in practically every case the suggestion was followed by sleep the same night.

It is very important to impress on these patients that, when bedtime comes, they are not to try to go to sleep. Their efforts merely produce a counter auto-suggestion that they will remain awake. I usually suggest that the patient will fall asleep five minutes after bedtime, and will be quite unable to wake until the night has passed. For some reason the suggestion seems to gain in strength in the time which elapses before the hour for its fulfilment.

5. *Nocturnal Enuresis.*—This can usually be cured by suggestion, and, curiously enough, sometimes by suggestion without any hypnosis whatever. From my own experience it has seemed to me that the form in which the suggestion is made causes a very considerable difference. The most effective suggestion I find is that the patient will not experience any desire to pass his water from the time he goes to bed until he gets up in the morning; a second suggestion may be made that if, by any accident, he should want to pass his water, he will always wake at once before he has actually commenced to do so.

6. *Frequent Micturition by Day.*—This is a very ordinary complaint, the patients being compelled to

pass their water at short intervals. I have never seen a case which could by hypnotism in the slightest degree fail to get well. In most cases improvement is seen at once, after the very first trial.

In one case sent me some five years ago by Mr. Thomson Walker, the patient was a lady, *æt.* 22, who was compelled to pass water every hour. The condition, which had persisted for eight years, made it quite impossible for her to go into society. After a single treatment she could retain her water for five hours, and has remained perfectly well ever since.

7. *Alcoholism.*—The aim of all treatment in alcoholism of whatever type is first to cut off alcohol if the patient be actually taking it, and then induce him to become a total abstainer, and, if possible, help him to do so.

This can be done partly by drugs, which induce a temporary dislike of alcohol, in the hope that the memory of the disgust of alcohol so engendered may become a permanent one ; and secondly, by moral treatment, including suggestion.

There are four principal forms of alcoholism : pseudo-dipsomania, chronic sober alcoholism, chronic inebriate alcoholism, and true dipsomania.

The pseudo-dipsomaniac has no craving until he has actually taken alcohol, when craving recurs, usually within a few minutes. He then drinks in great excess for several days, until he becomes too ill to take more. The chronic sober alcoholic drinks regularly every day to excess, but does not drink sufficiently to produce intoxication.

The chronic inebriate alcoholic differs from the last-mentioned, in that he always more or less is intoxicated. In the chronic alcoholic, craving occurs only when alcohol is partially or completely withheld.

The true dipsomaniac gets recurrent attacks of craving whether he takes alcohol or not. Between the attacks, many of these people can drink in moderation, but during the attacks they always drink to excess.

Whilst one can often successfully transform the pseudo-dipsomaniac or chronic alcoholic into a total abstainer, it is usually quite impossible to do this in a case of true dipsomania. Some cases appear to me to have their origin in the form of repressed gout, and I have seen six such cases in whom the taking of Contrexeville Water for three days running every fortnight, and a saline purgative once a week, has effectually stopped the attacks from recurring. Unfortunately in the majority of cases the cause is undiscoverable.

Two other forms of alcoholism, one occurring at menstruation in women, and the other due to insomnia, may be mentioned here. The first is often amenable to suggestion, and in the latter the curing of the insomnia usually puts an end to the alcoholism.

In one case a lady of over fifty had had persistent insomnia for seven years, and had drunk greatly in excess during the whole of that period. A single suggestion that she should sleep nine hours that night proved effective, and both the insomnia and the excessive drinking ceased at once, nor has there been any recurrence for seven years.

The cutting off. of alcohol in cases of chronic alcoholism must be done gradually; otherwise there is a very real risk of inducing delirium tremens. But for the medical side of treatment I must refer the reader to the literature on that subject.

Almost all the alcoholic patients whom I have seen have been susceptible to hypnotism, and in their case I certainly think that suggestion under hypnosis is more effectual than suggestion by Bramwell's method.

I usually treat these patients every day for eight days, two or three times on the few following weeks; once or twice in the week following that. After that, if possible, I see them at longer intervals for an indefinite term, and always enjoin them to come at once if they feel in the slightest degree that they are becoming less sure of themselves.

Some of my worst cases, who have now remained well for years, I have never seen after the first week or ten days of treatment. But these periodic visits are, I think, always advisable as a precautionary measure. Some patients come at intervals only when they begin to distrust themselves. One, who remained well for over twenty-five years, used to come about once in two years for this reason. If a patient begins to feel uncertain of himself, and does not then come for treatment, he usually does relapse. Out of over 300 patients treated about one-third remained well for a year or more, while just over one-fifth relapsed within a year. Of the remainder I was unable to trace the further history, and it is probable that some of these have relapsed, though one may reasonably hope that some are permanently well.

The following is à case of long standing, cured by suggestion.

Mr. J., æt. 52, had been a victim of chronic alcoholism for over thirty years. He habitually drank too much, usually whisky, and had recurrent fits of greater excess with marked intoxication; though even at ordinary times he was mildly intoxicated. I was asked by his medical attendant to see him while he was recovering from a specially bad attack which had made him exceedingly ill. He had twice tried the Normyl cure, but on both occasions abstained from alcohol only for a week or two after leaving it off. He had extremely advanced cirrhosis of his liver. I treated him ten times in all, and suggested that he would have no more craving, would dislike even the smell of liquor, and that his resolution and will power would increase sufficiently to enable him to resist any temptation to which he could possibly be subjected. He died some seven years later, but since his treatment he never again once touched alcohol.

More than this, he disliked the smell of whisky so much that if whisky and hot water were brought near him he could hardly endure the odour, and had actually been obliged to leave the room in consequence. I never treated him again after the first month, so that the result must have been due to the original suggestions. It is often said that women are more difficult to cure. This may be so: I have had comparatively few cases among women; but certainly some are not incurable. One very severe case, a lady of over fifty, has now been well for eight years, and another for over five years. But I certainly have had a less proportion of successes in women than in men. However, I have not had enough cases in women to form a fair judgment.

8. *Morphinomania.*—Suggestion is said to have been successful in this complaint, but its use is confined to helping the patients to abstain entirely. It does not appear to have any marked effect in relieving the symptoms induced by leaving off the drug, or in diminishing the time taken whilst it is being gradually discontinued. When the patient is once free from the habit it may help to prevent relapse, but more than this it cannot do. In cases of cocaine, if the patient be a confirmed cocaine taker, it is, so far as I have seen, almost impossible to ward off relapse by suggestion or any other means. Unlike morphia, however, cocaine may be cut off completely at once, and need not be gradually diminished.

9. *Sex Disorders*—(*a*) *Masturbation.*—This may occur as a habit in quite young children. I have seen several cases in which it commenced as early as five,

and some of these probably began even earlier. Provided that full sex development has not taken place, and that the patient wishes to break the habit, cure is extraordinarily easy. In later years, however, cure is a more difficult, and often a very gradual, process. Except in one case, of a boy of ten, with a marked family history of insanity, who did not wish to be cured, I have never failed when the patients were under thirteen years of age. In every one of these cases, with a single exception, the habit ceased at once after the first treatment.

The exception was the case of a girl *æt.* 7½, who had developed sexually at that early age, having suffered for over a year from very excessive masturbation. She was abnormally developed in every way, and weighed nearly seven stone. The habit had been taught her by another child.

On the second trial she passed into a light sleep, followed by amnesia. I saw her every day for a week, then twice a week for a fortnight. She improved greatly, remaining well for nearly a month, and then had a bad relapse. I then instructed her governess, of whom she was very fond, how to hypnotize her, and told her to do so when the child went to bed. In a few days all traces of the habit ceased, and, though there were some slight relapses, she was immensely improved, and of herself avoided the evil with all her might. I heard of her eight months later ; all traces of her former failing had absolutely disappeared, and she was perfectly well.

Both in children and adults it is of the greatest importance that they should understand clearly how they can cure themselves.

It is not of any use simply telling them to fight, for many have been fighting unsuccessfully for years. If the temptation occurs, and the patient thinks about it, and simply says: "I won't do it," he invariably yields. One has to recognize that the prime cause of many failures is the formation of a sex phantasy, and one's whole efforts must be directed to the prevention of this. Sex ideas, if dwelt upon, gain in force with terrific rapidity, and in almost a few seconds may result in irresistible impulse. The only way the patient can meet the temptation is not by direct resistance, which always results in defeat. He must run away from it, and direct his thoughts to something else—and this he must do instantly, within ten seconds of the occurrence of the sex idea. It is wonderful how very soon patients, even quite young children, learn to do this.

I never make any suggestion, except that they will be able to turn their thoughts away at once, and that they will find they have sufficient control to do this. In this way the actual origin of the evil—sex phantasy —can be prevented from developing. Naturally, it is more difficult for 'adults, and one must be prepared for slow progress, interrupted by many failures. But generally in these cases treatment will destroy the vice as a *habit*, even though there may be occasional lapses.

I have had considerable experience of boys at the time when they are most tempted, and I have very often found that, owing to the idea that they have done themselves really serious and irreparable injury, they have got into a condition of such despair that they are quite incapable of making any effort to cure themselves. This appears to me to be quite a false view, and not only false, but very mischievous. I have never been able to trace any physical results, except in cases of very great excess, and the mental and nervous condition is, I believe, entirely 'due to the fact that intense worry is produced by the feeling that the subjects cannot help themselves. But in nearly every case I believe that the fault lies not so much with the boy as with those who are responsible for his education. I have hardly ever met a case of this failing where sex instruction had been given before its development. In many cases it was begun in ignorance. A complete knowledge of the meaning of sex—without any reservations—not only satisfies a perfectly legitimate curiosity, but is the only real shield with which a parent can arm his sons to win in the battle which they will certainly have to fight.

(b) *Psychical Impotence.*—Anyone who practises suggestion is bound to come across numbers of cases of this complaint. Almost invariably the patients are men who have married, and have then discovered to their horror that they are impotent. The result is only too often extreme unhappiness, and I know of scarcely any other condition which gives rise to so much misery to' both the husband and wife. One patient whom I treated, fortunately with success, had actually attempted suicide.

The mental cause is, in the vast majority of cases, fear of non-success. But this is not always the reason; and, before a case of this kind can be treated with any hope of success, it is essential that the cause should be diagnosed. As a rule this can be done without any great difficulty, though some cases are exceedingly puzzling at first. In some—fortunately few—psycho-analysis alone can discover where the condition originates. The underlying cause is not always fear. It may be some form of sex perversion. In two cases which I saw, fetichism, which I could do nothing to remove, was the cause.

The fact that the condition may have persisted for a long time is not necessarily a bar to successful treatment. One case of seven-and-a-half years', and another of six years' duration, recovered completely. Most of the patients whom I have seen had suffered for from one to three years. In a certain number of cases suggestion is unnecessary. It is a strange and almost incredible fact that some patients were men of over thirty, who had no idea of the meaning of sex. Explanation in such cases may of itself sometimes effect a cure. But in the majority of cases the cause was the same. Failure from natural nervousness at the first attempt produced a fear of failure which was sufficient to render further attempts useless. In these cases I have found Yohimbin of use, though it often fails. The condition is often very obstinate, but practically all cases (except those where some insurmountable difficulty, such as perversion, exists) get well if treated rationally.

(c) *Primary Vaginismus.*—I have had cases of this complaint—all of which got well, probably because they happened to be particularly suitable cases for suggestion. In this, as in so many complaints, the cause is often a mental one, and must be discovered before treatment can be successfully applied.

(d) *Spasmodic Dysmenorrhœa* is sometimes readily curable. One patient, a lady of 23, had always been compelled to remain in bed during the whole of her periods ; but, after being treated three times, was able to remain up and follow her ordinary life. The pain became so slight as not to worry her.

I have not succeeded in relieving congestive dysmenorrhœa.

(e) *Absence of Sex Feeling* in women is usually readily curable, unless there is either some real congenital failing, or else some insuperable emotional cause for it.

I have had four cases in which treatment succeeded rapidly, but two, in which there was a feeling of repulsion towards the husband, failed to benefit.

10. *Stammering.*—At one time, owing to a succession of successful cases, I believed that this complaint could often be cured by suggestion. Further experience, however, has convinced me that it is in general some-

what difficult to cure permanently, though a transient improvement is not uncommon.

In this complaint I generally make the patient use self-suggestion, and teach him how to hypnotize himself lightly; and those who can learn this seem to be cured more easily than others.

In the case of a well-known German surgeon, whom I saw before the war, æt. 85, the stammering had persisted since early childhood. I taught him to hypnotize himself, and in three weeks his stammering had vanished.

Occasionally these patients recover and remain well after a single suggestion.

11. *Nervousness.*—The two cases following seem worth recording. The first patient was a man, æt. 28, who had failed at every examination owing to nervousness when the examination took place. I suggested that he would feel no nervousness whatever, and that when he looked at the questions he would at once recall all that he had read about them. He passed his examination, and told me that the suggestion with regard to remembering the facts had taken effect, and that he was much surprised at the amount he recollected. I have sometimes wondered whether I did wrong in making the experiment.

At Cambridge I once made a similar experiment on a man who was in for the Natural Science Tripos. The result of his examination was satisfactory, and he took first-class honours.

12. *Sea-Sickness.* — Sea-sickness can often be

successfully treated. I had during the war seven soldiers who had to go various distances by sea, and who had always suffered intensely from this complaint. Four were quite free from it after treatment, but of the result on the other three I know nothing, for all three lost their lives.

I have tried suggestion only in very few instances of sea-sickness. In one, which I saw some years ago, the effect was very marked. The patient had suffered severely every time she went to sea. I treated her six times just before she sailed for Cuba. She had no sickness during the whole journey, and never even felt sick, though the sea was occasionally very rough ; but she suffered severely from headache. She also complained that she was awakened from sleep by the slightest sound, but this symptom I failed to relieve. She reached only the first stage of hypnosis.

Suggestion is also said to relieve the vomiting of pregnancy, and cases have been published concerning this; but I have no experience in this matter myself.

13. *Chorea.*—Chorea has been successfully treated. Bramwell records seven instances of complete recovery, and other observers report numerous cases of cure.

In the three cases which I have treated, recovery took place in all; and there is no doubt that suggestion is sometimes very efficacious in this complaint.

14. *Insanity.*—The results in insanity are disap-

pointing. Personally, I usually refuse such cases, but some observers record successes.

Woods, in 1907, reported several cases of cure, comprising melancholia, puerperal mania, and ordinary mania.

15. *Constipation.*—I suppose that everyone who has used suggestion for this complaint has found it successful. So far as I have seen, the duration of a condition of chronic constipation is no bar to recovery through treatment by suggestion. I have seen cases which have recovered which had suffered for over forty years. The great majority do well, and failures are wonderfully few.

Forel names constipation as the typical functional disorder lending itself to treatment by suggestion. Probably many medical men have used suggestion for this disorder in the form of inert medicine described as aperient. It seems quite possible that the chief agent in much of the homœopathic pharmacy may be the labelling on the bottles. But we can often cure even chronic constipation quite readily by means of direct hypnotic suggestion.

The following case shows how very definite the results of a suggestion controlling the movements of the bowels may be: Mrs. R., aged thirty-five, came to consult me for intractable insomnia arising from mental anxiety, which had been very distressing for several weeks. I found that all her life she had been constipated, and for many years had never acted without an aperient. I did not hypnotize her, but suggested that she would sleep the moment she put her head on the pillow, and that her bowels would act next day and every day at ten o'clock in the morning, and requested her to come to see me again in three or four days' time. When I next saw her, she said that all had happened as I had suggested—that she slept the moment she went to bed, and that her bowels acted each day at ten o'clock. Then she added : "But would you mind making it half-past nine instead of ten o'clock. Ten is so inconvenient."

In many other cases the effect has been immediate and permanent. One patient, a lady of fifty-three, had suffered for over thirty years, and had been obliged to take medicine every night during the whole of that period. Yet, after the first suggestion, the constipation vanished, and she has remained cured now for seven years. Sometimes, however, the treatment fails, or else the improvement is merely temporary. It is sometimes best not to try at once to obtain a regular daily action, but to suggest an action every second or third day, and gradually to decrease the interval. In some cases the most one can do is to get an action every other day. This I have done in several cases, but long before I specialized in hypnotism, and I have no notes of them.

16. *Nervous Diarrhœa.*—This complaint is often confused with lientery, and no fewer than five cases which came to me were really suffering from this. For these I did not use suggestion, as liq.

arsenicalis in three-minim doses at once cured the condition.

As might be expected, diarrhœa of a purely nervous kind usually yields readily to suggestion.

Many patients get attacks only when some particular circumstance arises. One such patient, a surgeon, always got an attack before performing an abdominal operation, though operations on other regions did not affect him. Another patient was attacked if he had to make long journeys, and another was always obliged to refuse invitations to dinner, because, when the hour drew near, he invariably got acute diarrhœa. All these recovered after very few treatments.

Mr. A., a clerk, *æt.* 28, was subject to fits of diarrhœa from extremely slight causes, and had suffered in this way ever since his school-days. If he had to interview one of his chiefs he always had an attack, and the slightest deviation from his normal life, even the prospect of a journey, was sure to have this result. He was obviously of a very nervous temperament, and the idea of his visit to me brought on a severe paroxysm, his bowels acting five times that morning before I saw him. Hypnotized four times in June, 1898, he passed into deep somnambulism, and his nervous diarrhœa at once ceased. The causes which used to agitate him in this way were annulled, but slight exposure to cold seems to have been still followed by an attack. He left for South Africa shortly afterwards, and I hear from him that he remains well, though cold yet affects him.

Lloyd Tuckey records a striking instance of cure of chronic nervous diarrhœa in a patient aged seventy-two, who had been afflicted for many years, the disease dating from the time of the Crimean War.

17. *Spasmodic Asthma.*—In many cases of this complaint, even of very long standing, suggestion gives immediate relief, and prevents the onset of attacks during sleep:

If the patient be taught how to use self-suggestion he can generally cut short any threatened attack with the greatest ease.

This applies only to purely spasmodic asthma. If he attack be due to bronchitis or any irritation of the air tracts, suggestion is, so far as I have seen, of comparatively little use, though it may sometimes alleviate it to some extent.

18. *Epilepsy.*—I always refuse to treat it, believing that it is useless in such cases. Three cases, however, are worth mention, one of epilepsy and the other two of "petit mal." One epileptic was a young man who had one or more fits nearly every day. I found that he had nocturnal emissions every night. These ceased at once under the influence of suggestion, and his fits disappeared also, but recurred again as badly as ever some three months later, though the emissions did not return.

In two cases of "petit mal," in which the attacks occurred several times a day, I found that emissions took place every night. One was a man aged thirty-two, and the other forty. I stopped the emissions, and, to my surprise, the "petit mal". ceased, and has not recurred in either case. One has now been well for five years, and the other for nearly four years. What makes the case more curious is that the two patients were brothers.

In the only case of true epilepsy that I have tried; the patient, æt. 26, had suffered for twelve years, and the fits diminished from about one in eight days to about one a month; but I lost sight of him six months after treatment. I am inclined to think that the improvement must have been due to some cause other than the treatment.

V. Anæsthesia.

Suggested anæsthesia has been applied to various conditions. It has played the part of an anæsthetic in surgical operations, some of them of great severity, and has also been used to relieve pain, such as that of neuralgia, headache, and toothache, and even the agony caused by cancer. Confinements may also be rendered painless, without any of the disadvantages attendant on the use of chloroform.

As a rule, one cannot remove pain unless the patient has been trained by hypnotizations on previous occasions. But this is not always necessary. Many years ago, while at Cambridge, I happened one evening to call on Dr. W. H. Gaskell. He told me that his children's nurse was suffering from raging toothache, which had kept her awake for two nights, and he suggested that I should try to relieve her. She had been crying with pain, and the left side of her face was much swollen. I made her sit down, and told her that she was to look at my eyes, when she would fall asleep. She passed immediately into somnambulism, and I suggested the cessation of the pain, and awoke her. The pain had gone, but it came back in about an hour, this time, however, on the opposite side.* I removed it as before, and it never returned. She slept well that night, and Dr. Gaskell told me that next morning the swelling of her face had subsided.

Dr. Betts Taplin, of Liverpool, records a case in which he has succeeded in relieving the pain of cancer in the stomach. The diagnosis of cancer was confirmed by an exploratory operation. Under treatment by hypnosis, not only has the pain ceased, but the patient has put on flesh and eats well. Such a result is truly amazing.

As an anæsthetic during dental extraction hypnotism has been successfully employed, but its uncertainty and the necessity of the previous training of the patient are great disadvantages, so that it can never take the place of chloroform and ether. It has, however, as I said, frequently been used as an anæsthetic for confinements, and Dr. Bryan, of Leicester, has employed it most successfully for that purpose. He has also succeeded in regulating the supply of milk by means of suggestion, increasing or diminishing it, and even totally suppressing it at will. Employed thus, hypnotism might be extremely useful in the hands of those in general practice, since it is free from the dangers of chloroform.

Conclusion.

Although hypnotism may do much in beginning a cure, yet in many cases, especially in those which are somewhat vaguely classed as neurasthenias, much more is often required to make the regeneration complete and permanent. Only too many—their name is legion—owe their troubles to their unhealthy manner of life. Work they regard as an evil to be avoided as much as possible, and when they are sufficiently wealthy to be independent of it, as so many of these patients are, they have no regular occupation of any kind except pleasure-seeking, a pastime which is apt to pall as the years pass by. Distracted by ennui and imprisoned in self, they can remedy their condition only by a complete change of outlook on life, and their one hope of lasting cure lies in work and contact with the realities of life. If they can engender in themselves some human interest, they may forget their own sorrows in those of others. Until we have persuaded these patients to start a new life our work is only half finished. If the Valley of Achor be indeed a door of hope, it is our duty not only to open it and compel the dweller to pass through to the other side, but to lock and bar it against his return. In a word, we must, if possible, induce him to take up some absorbing form of labour, for in work, and work alone, will he find permanent salvation. " 'Je sais aussi,' dit Candide, ' qu'il faut cultiver notre jardin.' . . . 'Travaillons sans raisonner,' dit Martin, ' c'est le seul moyen de rendre la vie supportable.' "

CHAPTER VII

THE CASE AGAINST HYPNOTISM

Danger of unqualified and irresponsible use of hypnotism— Opinion of Moll—Question of liberty of subject to refuse suggestions—Conclusion.

HYPNOTISM, like nearly every other remedy powerful for good, may be mischievously used; but under the direction and authority of those who are qualified by knowledge and training, it is, I believe, an absolutely safe mode of treatment.

It is true that after hypnosis some patients may complain of heaviness and drowsiness, sometimes, it is said, of slight depression; but these symptoms may always be prevented by care in thoroughly dispelling the hypnosis at the time of awakening. Yet there is no doubt that, when the phenomena are used by travelling hypnotists merely for sensational show purposes, the results may be more harmful; and for this reason, if for no other, it is much to be desired that such exhibitions should be prohibited by law in this country, as they are in almost every other State in Europe. These people impose upon their subjects a succession of hallucinations of an exciting character, and sometimes do not thoroughly arouse them at the end of the performances. Some allow the subjects to believe that they may be influenced from a distance, and, if they are giving performances for several nights in succession, often compel those whom they find to be highly impressionable on the first occasion to attend the other displays by post-hypnotic suggestion.

Madam Card, who frequently performed in Cambridge, used to compel her undergraduate subjects to come to her séances in this way; and I believe that she herself had an idea that she could call them from afar—at least, I know that many thought she possessed this power.

The following instance exposes the harm which ensued on her proceedings. Mr. S., an undergraduate, attended one of her performances, was readily hypnotized by her, and made to do all kinds of absurd actions, while he also underwent a series of hallucinations, some of them of a more or less disturbing nature. The next day Madam Card left Cambridge. In the evening of that day the unfortunate victim was seized with the idea that she was staying at the Grosvenor Hotel in London, and was irresistibly calling for him. Go he would, but his friends forcibly detained him until the last train had left. He then, however, said that he must walk. I was asked to see him, and by a counter-suggestion cancelled the idea; but he was so much shaken by his experience that he was unable to undergo his examination on the following day. Presently he was well again, but the case impressed me very much as to the possible danger of hypnotism when carried out by ignorant persons. In other cases, too, Madam Card's subjects were made nervous and excitable for some hours after her performance.

The practice of hypnotism ought to be confined entirely to medical men and to serious and well-qualified scientific investigators. It is too potent an agent to be used as a plaything. Dr. Lloyd Tuckey gives in his book several cases in which harm has been wrought by those itinerant "professors." In one case he quotes Dr. M. J. Nolan's relation of a case of stuperose insanity, which he believes was caused by the ignorant employment of hypnotism, the patient, a drunken and dissipated soldier, broken in health by his excesses, having been hypnotized by a travelling operator. In another case which came under Dr. Tuckey's notice the patient had, after hypnotization, frequent cataleptic fits. In France serious epidemics of hysteria and other nervous affections are said to be observed after the visits of these itinerant showmen. But I know of no instance in which any evil consequence has followed the use of hypnotism by a properly qualified man for therapeutic purposes. It is open to exactly the same objections as other forms of treatment, and to no more, in that its irresponsible and uncomprehending use is likely to be followed by unpleasant and, in some cases, serious effects.

The real dangers of hypnotism, says Moll, are two

in number—the increased tendency to hypnosis, and
the heightened susceptibility to suggestion in the
waking state. The first, he says, is usually caused
by the use of Braid's method for the induction of
hypnosis, which, it will be remembered, consists in
making the subject fix his gaze for a time on some
bright object. For this reason, if for no other, it
is ill-suited for medical hypnosis. The other can be
guarded against by suggesting to the patient during
hypnosis that nobody can hypnotize him against his
will, and that nobody can enforce suggestions upon
him while he is awake—the surest way, says Moll, to
avoid this danger.

The question has been raised whether it may not
be possible by suggestion to compel a subject to carry
out some criminal act. Clearly this would constitute
a real danger only if the hypnotizer were of such a
character as to be capable of suggesting a crime, and,
as I imagine that no one would willingly be hypnotized
by a person of doubtful reputation, this does not
appear to be a very valid objection to the medical
use of hypnotic suggestion. But the question is an
interesting one, as it is possible that the plea of
hypnotic influence might be raised to shield the
accused in a criminal trial. Authorities are not
agreed as to whether this might be a real defence or
not. Bramwell states that even in somnambulism
he has never known a patient accept suggestions
which would not have been accepted in normal life,
and he gives instances where subjects have refused

even trivial suggestions, apparently because they conflicted with their ideas of propriety.

Forel, who has tried to make subjects commit experimental crimes, is inclined to think that these could be accomplished in waking life. Thus one subject was made, by suggestion, to fire twice at a man, the revolver being loaded, unknown to him, with blank cartridge. These experiments, however, are not conclusive, for it is impossible to be sure that the subject does not realize that they *are* only experiments, from which the operator has taken good care to eliminate any possibility of wrongdoing.

It is of interest to note that in no recorded case, as far as I know, has a subject in somnambulism ever refused an inhibitory suggestion, such as paralysis of a limb or the inability to carry out a given action. Personally, I doubt very much whether one could do so, and, until it is demonstrated that one can, I do not regard it as proved that patients can accept or reject every kind of suggestion at will. And even though it is certain that some subjects can resist certain imperative suggestions, it does not follow that all subjects can resist all repugnant suggestions.

Everyone with much experience of hypnotism must be familiar with the great variations in the degree of suggestibility in different subjects during somnambulism. It is scarcely surprising that some should be able to resist suggestions, whilst others cannot. The particular suggestions which are easily enforced vary much with different subjects, as also those suggestions which can be enforced only with difficulty or not at all.

But even if we assume, for the purpose of argument, that some people could be made to commit crimes (or, as has been asserted, to allow themselves to be criminally assaulted), it must be remembered that the number of such subjects must be very small. It may be safely asserted that such events could, under no circumstances, be possible unless the subject were somnambulistic, and under 20 per cent. pass into this condition. Even of these, very few would not at least try to resist such suggestions, and, as has already been shown, some, if not all, would do so successfully.

The question is at present an open one. Many deny altogether the existence of any danger of criminal suggestions, but other equally good authorities consider that the peril is not impossible. I am inclined to agree with Moll, who says : "Yet we must admit the possibility that a crime may be committed in this way, as Eulenburg, Dalley and Forel insist. On theoretical grounds I believe it is possible with some subjects. There may be much exaggeration. For example, few people are so susceptible as to accept the suggestion of a criminal act without repeated hypnotization. It is also true that many would refuse even after a long hypnotic training."

Liégeois also believed that criminal suggestions were not an impossibility.

But so long as they are recognized, even the slightest

risks of hypnotism can be readily avoided. It is essential that hypnotism should be employed with the same care and the same precautions as are required in the more dangerous process of giving anæsthetics. In each case some scientific knowledge and previous training are the only guarantees of safety, and so long as similar sureties are provided there can be no valid objection to the use of hypnotism as a remedial agent. The risks are few, the inconveniences trifling; and some maladies, such as dipsomania, can often be cured in no other way whatever.

Indeed, hypnotism, allied with a certain degree of psycho-analysis, seems the only kind of therapeutic power that can penetrate a certain obscure province of pathology at all. Only its relieving and strengthening suggestions, and its penetrative discoveries, can dissolve away the mortal matter when the mysterious nexus where the physical and psychical forces intercross becomes a core of anguish and corruption, can unravel the twisted knots of insubstantial yet intolerable pain in the dangerous net of the nerves, and harmonize those discords between bodily and spiritual life that beset a highly artificial and complicated state of civilization. When the senses practise strange tyrannies over the emotions and the will, or when the imaginative and intellectual powers maltreat the body into suppressed treacheries and revolts, psycho-analytic suggestion alone seems able to interpose in the confusion of consequent suffering. The dualism

of the remedy matches the dualism of the malady; it
is an instrument of which the peculiar nature and the
full consolatory virtues are not yet completely realized.
The physician in hypnotic suggestion, or trained
psycho-analysis, at least, need not altogether recoil
from the bitter outcry of Macbeth :

> "Canst thou not minister to a mind diseas'd,
> Pluck from the memory a rooted sorrow,
> Raze out the written troubles of the brain,
> And with some sweet oblivious antidote
> Cleanse the stuff'd bosom of that perilous stuff
> Which weighs upon the heart ?"

INDEX

BILLING AND SONS, LTD., PRINTERS, GUILDFORD, ENGLAND

Ingram Content Group UK Ltd.
Milton Keynes UK
UKHW052003110723
424865UK00009B/2